BEING SHEELA

Advance Praise

'For every door Sheela walks through, she holds it wide open for a generation of girls behind her. Her incredible life story—from an early call to fight injustice to becoming a powerful ally for the vulnerable and voiceless—reminds us all to hold tight to our values.'

—Leslie Mancuso, PhD, RN, FAAN,
President and Chief Executive Officer, Jhpiego

'Sheela is an inspiration to those of us advancing immigration justice. As a female lawyer, entrepreneur, philanthropist and mentor, she leads by example. For years, I have watched her lift up the voices of young people through the Fifth Grade Creative Writing Contest, encouraging them to speak their truth and nurturing a new generation of leaders. She has touched the lives of so many people by bringing empathy, persistence and pragmatism to everything she sets out to do.'

—Beth Werlin, Executive Director,
American Immigration Council

'Sheela Murthy's story demonstrates what happens when a person decides to put community first. Sheela's talent, perseverance and commitment to helping others has lifted up individuals, families and migrants from around the globe, making her book an inspirational read for anyone looking to make a difference in today's complex world.'

—Brian A. Gallagher, President and CEO,
United Way Worldwide

'Sheela and I go back more than three decades. She was a well-known name in University Law College, Bangalore, where I studied. By the time I had joined college, she had already moved to the US. When we qualified for the Philip C. Jessup Moot court competition to be held in Chicago, Sheela was our go-to person. She helped us through our entire trip and even hosted us at her place in New York.

'Sheela is a gritty lady with a soft heart. Despite being busy, she is a family person to the core who makes it a point to spend time with her mother and sisters in Bangalore. We have spent some great times together during her recent visits to India. The one thing she believes in is to live life to the fullest.

'Professionally, Sheela is simply brilliant! She has won accolades for herself and made both her family and friends proud. Her philanthropic side is truly commendable.

'Sheela Murthy's biography is a great venture to inspire young girls who intend to choose a career in law.'

—Justice Prathiba M. Singh, Judge,
Delhi High Court, India

'From the young girl described as unusual and brave to the young woman who becomes an acclaimed international lawyer and generous philanthropist, Sheela Murthy's story inspires and reminds us why we are proud to be known as a nation of immigrants.'

—Kurt L. Schmoke, President, University of
Baltimore and former Mayor of Baltimore

'A powerful and riveting book that showcases the struggles of immigrants, and how Sheela Murthy, with her grit and determination, has made a difference and changed lives. Sheela's life story, love, passion and work, are all intertwined beautifully, to motivate and inspire us to do more to help our fellow human beings.'

—Patricia M.C. Brown, former President of Johns Hopkins
Healthcare LLC and Senior VP, Johns Hopkins Medicine

'Sheela Murthy has followed a path from her beloved India to America—from immigrant to immigration lawyer and compassionate advisor to those dealing with the system. Although a giant of American immigration law, she has never lost touch with her native land and the need to help others—no matter what their origin—surmount immigration hurdles. *Being Sheela* is the story of her impact and success, and of her acts of philanthropy. She has been blessed with much and blesses others with her resources, caring and support.'

—Ron Shapiro, attorney, negotiations expert, community leader and *New York Times* bestselling author

'Sheela is one of the stars in American immigration law. She has made extraordinary contributions, including at Harvard Law School, where she has funded scholarships for graduate students. She has supported our immigration clinic in countless ways, including providing training opportunities for our clinicians.'

—Deborah Anker, Clinical Professor of Law, Harvard Law School and founder of the Harvard Immigration and Refugee Clinical Program

'Sheela Murthy has been instrumental in protecting several companies and individuals, with the ever-changing immigration rules and regulations. A dedicated entrepreneur and philanthropist in modern history with a strong will to stand up against injustice, we give huge credit to Sheela Murthy for the ITSERVE victory, which resulted in the USCIS issuance of the ITSERVE memo in 2020.'

—Amar Varada, President, ITSERVE Alliance and President, Surya Systems

'Sheela has excelled in everything she has done, not only professionally, but in inspiring others to do their best. Sheela has done so many things that I am sure every reader will find a direct connection to at least some part of her life. The best of Sheela is yet to come.'

—Desh Deshpande, Life Member, MIT Corporation; serial entrepreneur; Trustee, Deshpande Foundation

BEING
SHEELA

The Life Journey *of*
an Immigration Lawyer

ADITHI RAO

HarperCollins *Publishers* India

First published in India by
HarperCollins *Publishers* in 2020
A-75, Sector 57, Noida, Uttar Pradesh 201301, India
www.harpercollins.co.in

2 4 6 8 10 9 7 5 3 1

P-ISBN: 978-93-9032-799-7
E-ISBN: 978-93-9027-982-1

Typeset in 11.5/15.2 Adobe Garamond Pro at
Manipal Technologies Limited, Manipal

Printed and bound at
Thomson Press (India) Ltd.

MIX
Paper
FSC™ C010615

This book is produced from independently certified FSC™ paper
to ensure responsible forest management.

For Mrs Sheila Rao
Beloved aunt & friend,
Whose counsel and support are the foundations upon
which this book was built.

—Adithi Rao

* * *

My mother, Indu Murthy, whose unwavering drive and ambition for
all her three daughters was for them to become strong, successful and
financially independent women. I am not sure that any of us can ever
make her truly happy, but, Mom, I sure did try my best.

My husband, Vasant Nayak, whose steadfast love, guidance,
friendship and support has meant the world to me.

—Sheela Murthy

TELL ME A STORY

The rain splashes down
It covers the world
Like a blanket of water
That's been gently unfurled
Like a hand on the window
Knocking to come in
I open my book
I'm ready to begin

But the book has no words,
Not a single one at all
I drop the book
And watch it fall
I grab my coat
And head for the door
I'm searching for stories
I'm searching for more

Up the avenue
Across the street
Lies an old house

With people to meet
Wind in my hair
Hope in my eyes
My Abuela steps onto the porch
Where a story lies

'Tell me a story.'
That's what I say
To my grandmother
On that rainy day
She responds with a smile
And points to a chair
Abuela begins
As rain splashes her hair

She tells of festivals,
Dances and lights,
Fiestas and siestas
On warm summer nights
'This is my story.'
Abuela starts to explain
'I was a little girl
Living in Spain.'

'Why did you leave?'
I wonder aloud
Her shoulders square
Tall and proud
'There was a war
That broke out
Our family fled
And traveled about

Looking for a home,
Safe and sound

'America
Was the land we finally found
I met new people
From all different places
Everyone was unique
All different races.'

Her smile twinkles
And a tear slips by
'America is beautiful'
Is all I reply

'America is beautiful.'
Abuela says loud and bold
'Every immigrant has a story
and every story must get told.'
I listen as her words fill my heart
Every culture is beautiful
Like a piece of art
I smile to myself
Knowing that it's true
'America is beautiful
Because of immigrants like you.'
I look at Abuela
As I utter these words
She simply points to the sky
She points at the birds
The eagles glide
And soar through the air

A rustle of wind
Blows through my hair
I step off the porch
To get a better view
Abuela smiles
And steps down, too
Our eyes meet
As Abuela starts to speak
She grabs my hand
And the eagles reach their peak
'You have to stay strong
Like an eagle with might
When things get tough
You have to fight.'

'Thank you!'
I call as I start to leave
I know what to do
I have a story to weave

Down the avenue
Across the street
Lies my house
With people to greet
Hope in my eyes
Wind in my hair
I rush inside

I dash to my bedroom
Pick the book off the floor
And write Abuela's story

Until my hand is sore
I think about Abuela,
America's glory,
And immigrants' impact
On our country's story

I'm busy working
When I hear a knock
'Come in!' I call
The only response is a quiet walk
I set down my pen
My sister walks in
She asks for a story
And so, I begin...

—Kate Jentz of Carmel, Indiana
(Winner of 'Celebrate America Creative Writing Contest' 2019
Theme: *Why I Am Grateful America is a Nation of Immigrants*)

1

Somebody once described Sheela Murthy as a connoisseur of immigration law. The usual term, you'd think, would have been 'expert'. However, Sheela not only knew immigration law like the back of her hand, but also *relished* it. It was the thing that made her heart beat and the blood pump in her veins. Very few other things in this world could captivate her in a similar way.

Gazing out of the window, from her comfortable first-floor office at the Murthy Law Firm, she waited for her 11 a.m. appointment to arrive. It was 11.03 already, and Sheela was concerned that she would not get sufficient time to speak with this client before her next appointment arrived. When clients walked in, they were often troubled, tired, sad, or desperate, and at times all those things at once. And Sheela was determined to do whatever it took to help them. Only, a late arrival would make it so much more difficult.

The door opened and her husband, Vasant, poked his head around it.

'Tea, Sheelu?' he asked in his quiet, affectionate way, and the sight of him made her heart lift as always. She nodded enthusiastically. Any time was a good time for a cup of piping hot tea, in her opinion! And if a samosa came along with it then even better!

When he went off to fetch them each a cup, Sheela fell to thinking. 'Here we are, working in this beautiful building, with its chairs and desks, computers and office equipment. Then there are the pens, the staplers, and other stationery that we use all day long. And if one were to take an inventory of the office, they would put down most of those things in its list of assets. One may even add the large signage at the top of the building that reads Murthy Law Firm. But then there is Vasant, and the happiness of a cup of tea with him in the middle of a busy morning. There's Aron, Adam, Pam, Anna, Khorzad, Joel, and all the others who work here; the trust and friendship that we all share. And there's the sun shining in through my window on this beautiful chilly, Baltimore morning. Nobody would ever think of putting those on the list, would they? Someone should take a separate inventory for happiness. Just so there'd be something to look at when things get us down.'

As she sat deep in thoughts, piping hot tea arrived and was sipped slowly over a conversation about the parents in faraway India. Just as Sheela placed her empty cup back on the table, the client arrived.

* * *

The lady sitting across the desk from Sheela Murthy was thirty-four years old. She looked fifty. As Sheela listened to her speak, she thought to herself, 'It's because of the sadness in her eyes.'

'My name is Vijaya Prasad, madam,' said the lady. The Indian accent had lingered on her tongue despite her eight years in America. Sheela wanted to tell her to call her by first name, but knew from experience that the Indian sense of propriety would not permit Vijaya to do so easily.

'Vijaya,' said the lady, 'from Vijayawada, originally.' Then she added with a smile, 'Yes, you too must be thinking that it is funny, no? Vijaya from Vijayawada. My parents named me that on purpose.

"So that you'll never forget your roots, Viji," they used to say to me when I was a little girl. As if I could ever forget, madam.'

There followed a moment of silence, as Sheela waited for the woman to tell her story, from the beginning, as some clients preferred to do.

'Soon after I finished my Masters in Computer Programing, my parents introduced me to a man from Hyderabad. He was a good man and soon we got married. We were happy together.'

Was. Were. Sheela noted the use of the past tense and thought she now understood the air of sadness that this woman seemed to wear like a mantle on her shoulders—a mantle that didn't seem as if it was taken off for even a minute.

'We had four children,' went on Vijaya. 'Three girls and one boy. He was a good father, he loved them very much. When he was dying, he cried because he was so sorry to leave me alone to raise the children all by myself.'

Vijaya paused again, this time to fight back the tears.

'Would you like some tea or a cup of coffee, perhaps?' asked Sheela.

'No madam, thank you. Already I have come in so late. I was delayed with a client at work. I don't want to waste any more of your time.'

'Don't worry about it,' said Sheela, 'Please go on.' Over the woman's half-hearted protests, she requested Amanda, her executive assistant, to bring a cup of tea for Vijaya. So many similar clients crossed Sheela's threshold each week, and nearly always, she had a solution for them. But there were times when she did not. Yet they were never sent away without the comfort of a hot beverage cradled between chilled palms, the warmth of her smile, and good, solid advice on how to make the best of a difficult situation. And that way, it would not be a complete loss, even if it could not be a win.

Today, it was Vijaya's turn to sit across from her and Sheela prayed that she would be able to give her a solution that would lessen the sadness in her eyes.

'My children and I moved back to Vijayawada to live with my parents because my husband's family did not want to have anything to do with us after his death. You see, my husband had incurred heavy debts in his business, and his parents did not want the responsibility of paying them off. So, after the funeral, they left and never contacted me or their grandchildren again.'

Sheela felt anger stir inside her, but firmly pushed it aside. She had learnt, in her decades of work as an immigration lawyer, that bad things happened to good people every day. It was an unfair world. Losing her calm would only cloud her judgment when the time came to help her client in the best possible way. In Vijaya's case, it was clear that she had not even got to the actual problem yet.

'My parents were heartbroken. But they tried to appear cheerful because they wanted to be strong for me. I got myself a job. After I returned home from the office in the evenings, I took up private tutorials coaching school children in math and science. I spent most of my earnings on my children's education and in running our home. But I kept aside a little every month to hand over to my husband's creditors. They soon saw that I honestly meant to pay them back, and that I had no intention of defaulting. I told them that it would take me time, but I would not stop until every last rupee my husband owed them had been returned. They were good people and felt sorry for me, so they did not trouble me to pay more than I could afford to each month.

'The children were growing up well; my parents took good care of them while I was at work. I tell you, madam, I don't know what I would have done without their support.'

Sheela knew what the affection of a grandparent could mean to a lonely child. Four of them in this case. Her heart went out to them.

'Then, my best friend, Tara, who had been studying in the US for some years, met a man who was already working here and decided to marry him. Their families had consented to their marrying in the US and intended to travel from India for the ceremony. Tara asked me to join them but I could not afford the ticket. So she bought the ticket for me, and her insistence made it difficult for me to refuse. Now I had no choice but to agree. I went to the consulate in Hyderabad, and they issued a visitor's visa to me. I held my children close, feeling terrible about leaving them, even though it was only for a week. That was eight years ago, madam. I haven't seen them since.'

2

Sheela had been expecting many things. But she hadn't been prepared for what Vijaya told her. *Eight* years? To the two-year-old son, now ten, that was practically his whole life that he hadn't seen his mother. Did he even remember Vijaya? The smell of her? The feel of her hand patting him to sleep at night?

As Sheela was contemplating this fact, she was suddenly interrupted by the buzzer on the intercom. 'Sorry, Amanda,' said Sheela, leaning forward to speak into the instrument while keeping her eyes on the wan face before her. 'I need a few more minutes. Could you ask Mr Anderson to wait, please? I need another ten minutes.'

'Sure, Sheela,' mumbled Amanda, and disconnected the line. She knew it must be really important, whatever was going on inside the room, because Sheela was generally very particular about keeping her time commitments.

'You were saying, Vijaya?' nodded Sheela encouragingly.

'The wedding was in Boston. At the reception, I was introduced to the man that the bridegroom worked for. He spent a few minutes talking to me, asking me about my work. When he found out what I did, he got very excited. He said that he had a position in his firm that he had been trying to fill for a long time but had not been able to find someone with the right skills. The position involved the exact kind of work as I was doing at my company in India. He offered a terrific salary if I agreed to join immediately. There was a potentially large client waiting that they didn't want to lose, and if I would agree to take over the project as soon as the company obtained the H-1B approval for me, then they would be able to sign on the client and be ready to begin work.'

Sheela nodded. 'He offered to sponsor your H-1B, of course?'

'Yes. The company filed a petition for change of status from a B-2 to an H-1B from within the US, and it came through within a couple of weeks.'

Sheela frowned. 'What is the problem then, Vijaya?'

'In the first three years of working in the US, I paid off all the debts that my husband had incurred. After that I began to save up until I could afford to move out of the apartment that I had been sharing with three other women. I rented a small, comfortable home for my children in a safe neighborhood. Then I sent the paperwork for my children to apply for their H-4 dependent visas. I wanted them to come and live with me; it had been so many years since I had seen them! I also wanted to relieve my old parents of the responsibility. Over and over again they applied, madam. But each time their visas were turned down. The American consulate in Hyderabad has laid down the condition that I must return to India and be present there physically to apply for the H-4 visas for my children. They say that they would like to understand why I had entered the United States on a tourist visa and remained behind for so many years after that. They said...'

Here Vijaya spread open a piece of paper that she had unconsciously crumpled into a ball in the palm of her sweaty hand, and read aloud from it: 'They said that I had "misrepresented my temporary non-immigration intention at the time of applying for my B-2 tourist visa, when I had first entered the United States".'

Vijaya looked up from the paper and directly into Sheela's eyes. 'I never came to the US with any reason other than to attend Tara's wedding, madam. Whatever happened after that was just fate. You must believe me!'

'I do believe you,' said Sheela.

* * *

After the business with Mr Anderson was completed, Sheela left and joined the rest of the team for lunch. Today was pizza day. Sheela's boundless love for food was no secret. When she pulled up a chair beside him, Joel Yanovich, the firm's Attorney Coordinator of the General Legal Department, began telling Sheela the latest about his baby Sagan. Sheela loved the little fellow and was usually always interested in any new milestone that he had achieved. However, that afternoon Joel spoke for a full five minutes without eliciting any response beyond an absent 'hmm' here and an occasional 'oh' there. He figured that she was deeply engrossed in her thoughts when she rose to wash her plate after just one slice of the pizza (two less than her usual quota!). So, shut up he did, as it would only be kind to leave her with her thoughts. Barely noticing his silence, Sheela absently put away her plate in the kitchenette and returned to her office.

She immediately picked up the phone and waited for Amanda to answer when she remembered that her EA was still at lunch, eating with the others. So, Sheela headed out for a short walk.

Murthy Law Firm had an affiliated office by the name Murthy Immigration Services Private Limited, also referred to at times as MISPL, in Chennai, India. Sheela made it a point to travel to her home country two, sometimes three, times a year for the dual purpose of spending a few weeks with her family and visiting the liaison office to check up on things there. While in India, she made it a point to meet the consular officers at the United States Consulates in Chennai, Mumbai and Hyderabad, and spend time with them in person. Many of her clients hailed from places that had to go through the American Consulates situated in one or the other of these cities for their visa interviews, and Sheela knew that keeping herself abreast with changes in their policies and procedures, and maintaining a good working relationship with the officers, went a long way in helping her clients when something needed getting done. This was particularly so in cases where there was a need for discretion, as it certainly was in the case of Vijaya. They knew her to be a lawyer with high integrity and often took her word on behalf of a client. Likewise, Sheela never took advantage of the professional relationship she had established with consular officers over the years, and the trust they placed in her.

Having collected her thoughts during the walk, Sheela was now once again seated at her desk, logged into her computer. She wrote an email to the consular officer in Hyderabad, India. After opening with the usual formal niceties, the email said:

'It is my understanding that in order to issue the H-4 visas for her children, you require Mrs Vijaya Prasad to return to India to apply for her H-1B visa. Under the law, such a requirement is not justified when she has already been in the United States these past eight years on a valid H-1B status. Therefore, we would very much appreciate your insights, and your providing us the legal basis for your decision.'

3

Three days later, in the same chair that Vijaya occupied in the conference room, sat a man sporting a moustache à la Groucho Marx. He took a deep breath and said with an impressive gravity, 'It is a very serious matter that I have come to consult you about, Ms Murthy.'

'Tell me,' said Sheela.

'I am planning to apply for my green card,' said Bharat, sitting up straighter and looking at her expectantly.

'I see.'

'That is, I plan to apply for my green card through four different companies!'

Now it was Sheela's turn to sit up straight. She leaned forward, curious about what would follow. Of course, this was not the first time she had heard of people applying through more than one company, and it wouldn't be the last time either. But *four* companies! Sheela had to admit that was a first.

'And what is your question, Bharat?'

'I want to know whether it is a good idea.'

Sheela sat back with an inward sigh. 'You're from Mumbai?'

'Yes,' replied Bharat.

'Do you know Rupesh?' she asked, randomly picking a name that she knew was common in those parts.

'Er ... Rupesh ... yes,' the young man replied, flummoxed by the sudden change in topic. 'You're asking about Rupesh Sharma? Or else ... I mean, which Rupesh? ... I know two, but...'

'Some time ago, he put out a matrimonial ad in the newspaper and received several responses,' Sheela cut across him. 'But he was apprehensive that he would never find the right girl to marry, and so he got in touch with everyone who responded to his ad, met several girls, and finally fixed on four.'

'*Four?*'

'Yes, four,' said Sheela.

'Bastard!' said Bharat with an admiring laugh, then immediately slapped his hand over his mouth in dismay at as he realized the invective that he had let slip. Sheela ignored the faux pas and continued as if he had not spoken.

'He met each of those girls' parents, promised to marry, and even agreed upon the dates for the engagement ceremonies. It just so happened that three of the girls' fathers were acquainted. So, when they printed the invitation cards, they invited each other to their daughters' weddings and discovered that the name of the bridegroom was the same on each card. It seemed that they were all about to have a mutual son-in-law!'

Bharat's mouth was slightly open and his eyes now appeared a little glazed.

'As you can imagine, Bharat, all the three fathers cancelled the wedding and spread the word about Rupesh's trickery around in their community. Soon Rupesh found himself blacklisted by every marriage broker and from every matrimonial site. Every time he tried to arrange an alliance for himself, the parents of the prospective girls found out about his wrongdoings and refused to let him meet with their daughters. It's been five years. He remains single to this day.'

In the silence that followed, the analogy sank in, and Bharat suddenly came to his senses. He snapped his mouth shut, nodded, and smiled suavely, trying to appear casual.

'Good story! Interesting. Hmm. Interesting,' he said. 'Anyway, so the *real* reason I came, was to consult you over a different matter—'

'Bharat?' cut in Sheela, not unkindly.

'Hmm?'

'Your twenty minutes are up. Another twenty minutes will cost you a further $300. Are you sure you would like to continue?'

'Er, no ma'am!' said Bharat and quickly got to his feet. 'I got all the information I needed. Er ... thank you!'

As he hurried to the door, Sheela called out, 'And Bharat...'

'Yes?'

'That person I was telling you about? Rupesh was not a bad person. Just impatient. But in the long run, patience works better.'

Bharat looked at her from across the conference room, and she smiled. Nodding, he left, shutting the door carefully behind him. Leaning forward to speak into the intercom, Sheela said, 'Amanda?'

'Yes, Sheela?'

'Please refund the 300-dollar consultation fee that Bharat transferred to us for this afternoon's appointment.'

'Are you sure?' asked Amanda in surprise.

'Very. I really did not give him any legal advice, just some sound counsel that should help him in life. One can't charge a man a fee for his desperation.'

4

'I have Matthew Stern from the US Department of State.'

'Thank you, Amanda, please put me through.'

'Hi Matthew, Sheela Murthy here. I hope you're doing well?'

'I'm great, Sheela!' replied Matthew Stern, chief of the Legal Advisory Opinion Section of the US Department of State's Visa Office. 'And you?'

'Very good too, Matt!' Sheela's characteristic warm smile was evident in her voice. 'I called because I wanted to bring a matter to your notice.'

She explained that she had sent an email but had not heard back from the US Consulate in Hyderabad. She then proceeded to outline the details of the Vijaya Prasad case, briefly but clearly, as was her style. She concluded by saying,

'Although I understand the consular officer's concern that the mother may have provided information contrary to her actions, I have spent considerable time getting to know the circumstances of this case. It is my understanding that Vijaya genuinely came into this country with the intention of returning to India within a few days. But when she was unexpectedly offered a good job, she simply couldn't turn it down. Her financial and personal situations back in India were too dire. Four kids, huge debts left behind by her late husband, and no other financial support. In fact, Matt, things were so bad that for the first three years in the US she shared an apartment with three other women and walked to work each day so that she could send every penny back home to pay off the debts and the school fee for her kids. It took her three years to be able to apply for the H-4 visas for the children to have them join her in this country. But putting all that aside, my argument is that there is nothing in the statute or the regulations that would permit denying H-4 dependent visas to minor children or requiring the mother to return to Hyderabad for a personal interview at the US Consulate there.'

There was a long pause. Then Matthew asked, 'What would you like me to do?'

'I would be grateful if you could request the US Consulate in Hyderabad to issue the H-4 visas to her children as quickly as possible. This is a mother whose youngest child was two years old when she left, Matthew. The child is ten years old now.'

The plea in her voice was unmistakable, and Matthew sighed. He had no reason to doubt Sheela's word because her reputation for honesty in all her dealings was impeccable. Plus, she was right regarding the law. 'I'll see what can be done,' he said, and something about the way he said it made Sheela know, deep down, that the job was already done. She closed her eyes and took a long, steadying breath. A sense of relief washed over her, dispelling the niggling sadness she had carried inside her heart since the day Vijaya, from Vijayawada, had first walked into her office.

In a few weeks' time, or maybe within a few days, somewhere out there in the city of Baltimore, a mother would get to hold her children in her arms again.

5

Back in 1963, during a visit to a relative's home, Captain H.M.S. Murthy sipped whiskey and discussed politics with his cousin. His wife Indu, had joined the cousin's wife in the kitchen, and their voices floated out to the menfolk in the living room; the latter was complaining about the migraine headaches that frequently afflicted her and Indu was suggesting a remedy of the tinctures of *Damiana* and *Passiflora* to combat it. She was deeply interested in the science of Homeopathy and often experimented with it.

All the while, Captain Murthy's eyes kept straying to his two-year-old daughter, Sheela, as she played on the carpet with his cousin's baby. So fascinated was he by the way in which his daughter carefully held the feeding bottle to the infant's mouth that his cousin's voice and speculations about the theft that had taken place at the Hazratbal shrine just the previous day faded into the background. Sheela's small hand, weary as it must have been, never shook or faltered once. Captain Murthy saw the determination on her face, the glow in her eyes as she gazed down at the baby. And he knew, for the first time that day, that there was something special about Sheela. She had courage and a fierce ability to love beyond her own limitations that set her apart from every other child he knew, including his older daughter, Shree.

When it was time to go, Captain Murthy rose to his feet and took leave of the cousin. Sheela looked up at her father with bright, hopeful eyes and asked, 'Can we take this baby home, Daddy?'

Indu Murthy, who had joined her husband in the living room in preparation for their departure, hurried forward and steered her daughter towards the front door saying with a small, embarrassed laugh, 'It is not our baby, Sheela! We can't take it home with us.'

Sheela's smile faltered. But she did not protest as her mother marched her outside to Daddy's scooter parked in the driveway. For some months now, every time the family came in contact with people who had babies, Sheela begged to be allowed to take the baby home. And her parents responded with the exact same words: 'It is not ours. We can't take it with us.'

Back at home, Sheela sat gazing upon her doll—the only ragged toy that her parents had been able to afford for their girls, to be shared between them. Sometime later, Mummy announced dinner. When the family of four had gathered around the table, Sheela silently nibbled the food that her mother had put on a plate in front of her. Only Daddy, ever watchful of his child, noticed her sadness. Indu, impatient even in the best of times and constantly preoccupied with trying to run a household on money that never seemed to last the entire month, took no notice. Neither did she resort to the nursery rhymes and fairy tales that parents often employ to make food go down quicker. That was Captain Murthy's department. Making them roll with laugher over his silly jokes and delightful anecdotes, wiping snotty noses, sometimes with the underside of his shirt when Indu wasn't looking and listening to their childhood secrets—all these jobs came under Captain Murthy's department and he performed them with all his heart.

But for all this, he had to be home, which was often not the case.

Indu's area of operation, on the other hand, was cooking strictly balanced meals for her family and ensuring that her children were clean, healthy, disciplined and well-mannered, *at all times*. As the girls grew up, it also became Indu's special task to make sure they were up-to-date with their homework and fared well in the school exams. She did not hesitate to use the rolling pin on them to get the desired results. In fact, the rolling pin was never put away into the drawer, but was left outside on the kitchen countertop so that she could grab it in a jiffy, whenever needed. And she seemed to need it quite often!

That night, when dinner was over, Captain Murthy watched Sheela as she slipped off her chair, washed her hands meticulously with soap and water just as she had been taught to do by Mummy, and returned to the tiny room she shared with Shree. There, she picked up her doll and carefully put it into a bag.

'What is she doing?' demanded five-year-old Shree, hurrying forward to stop her. But her father held her back.

'Let her be,' he murmured, never taking his eyes off Sheela. 'She already knows the difference between make-believe and the real thing, and she is not willing to settle.'

* * *

The soft white curtains were drawn down the middle of the room. Everything behind it appeared hazy, luminescent and ethereal, just as it would be in a dream. Captain Murthy led his daughters inside, tiptoeing so as not to make any noise. The air of anticipation was more than what a three-year-old Sheela could bear!

Just behind the curtain, on a single metal bed furnished with blue hospital sheets, Indu lay asleep. Her chest rose and fell steadily, and the tightness that had gripped Sheela's heart since Mummy had been whisked away to the hospital the previous night, eased a little. Mummy was all right, then! Mummy had not left and gone away! Sheela blinked back tears and looked at her father, who smiled down at her.

He took her hand and led her to a small metal crib placed in one corner of the room. The crib was moving from side to side in tiny jerks, all on its very own; faint, mewling sounds were coming from it. Captain Murthy bent down and lifted Sheela so she could look inside the crib. There was a baby! A tiny being with eyes tightly closed, moving its head from side to side as if its mouth searched for something.

Slowly raising her wondering eyes to her father, she whispered, 'Is this our baby, Daddy? Can we take it home?'

'Not *our* baby, Sheela,' replied Daddy. 'This is *your* baby, your little sister. And yes, you can take her home.'

* * *

From the moment they brought baby Suman home from the hospital there was little for Indu and Captain Murthy to do. Sheela took over the care of the infant with a completeness that left her father enamored and her mother ... well, anxious.

'*Haagey helubardittu!*' exclaimed Indu in her native tongue to her husband when one day, two years after Suman's birth, she came into the bedroom to check Suman's diaper and found Sheela changing it with astounding ease. For a while now she had observed, with growing trepidation, Sheela's all-consuming commitment to her little sister. At first the mother had laughed it off as a passing fancy. But when time did nothing to cool the initial fervor of what she had assumed to be a child's obsession with a new toy, Indu became seriously concerned.

'*Haagey helubardittu*! You should never have told Sheela that the baby was hers,' she scolded her husband.

At the tone of her voice, Captain Murthy looked up from his newspaper in alarm. Tranquil and easygoing as he was, he was well acquainted with his wife's temper and hated being around to face it if there was the slightest excuse for him to be elsewhere. Unfortunately, at 7 a.m. on a Sunday, there were few reasons to be elsewhere other than on the front porch of their two-bedroom army residential quarters in the city of Allahabad, where he happened to be stationed at that time.

Wondering whether he was about to make the mistake of his life, he nevertheless ventured to do so by inquiring mildly, 'What is the problem, Indu?'

His fears, however, came true as she unleashed upon him the sum total of her indignation of the past two years. 'Which man puts a three-year-old in charge of a newborn?' she demanded, glowering at him. 'I heard you telling her that it was *her* baby, back then at the hospital the day Suman was born! You thought I was asleep but I heard you. And now this nonsense has been going on for two whole years!'

Her tiny frame assumed monstrous proportions in his imagination, even though, when seated in his rocking chair, the top of his head was on level with her chin.

'But Indu, it made her so happy...'

'Happy? She has given up playing, studying, eating, everything she loved doing, just to sit inside the house all day long and take care of Suman! Changing diapers is a parent's job, not hers. She should be outside running around with her friends! How could you not know that?'

At her raised voice, Sheela looked around in alarm. Her mother's stringent tone always made her heart go cold. She could take Mummy scolding her but when she scolded Daddy, Sheela just couldn't bear it. She knew that Daddy usually disappeared for long hours after such instances. What if someday he went away and never returned? Sheela couldn't bear the thought of living in the house without her darling, happy-go-lucky father. It would never feel like home again without him.

Shree was pleasant enough, sharing her books with Sheela and patting her head from time to time. But it just wasn't the same as having Daddy's arms to snuggle into, his ears to pour her secrets into. After all, Shree was lost in her own world for the most part—vague and often withdrawn, forgetting to eat, forgetting to play, forgetting even to run away when their mother picked up the rolling pin! There seemed to be little room in Shree's life for a younger sibling, let alone two!

That day, like many other days in the past, Sheela's fears proved right. It turned out to be one of those days when Captain Murthy slipped away from the house, taking refuge in whiskey and the card table at the officer's club, only to return long after Sheela had gone to sleep, curled up beside her baby sister for comfort.

However, this time around, Indu did have a point. Until the advent of Suman, Sheela's life was a joyous exuberance, filled with a tomboy's delight in climbing trees, playing with the neighbor's boy, floating paper boats in the nearby streams with the children of the *jawans*, scraping her knees while crawling up the hillsides with her mates, and stealing fruits from the neighbors' gardens.

Indu had watched, with increasing alarm, her second daughter turn sedate around Suman. It didn't help that Suman adored her older sister and followed her everywhere like a shadow! That only made Sheela all the more committed to the child. But by and by, as Suman grew up, Sheela slowly went back to her old boisterous self, taking Suman with her. As they ran through the house screaming with laughter and turning the furniture upside down, Indu was hard-pressed to maintain the discipline and cleanliness she was so particular about. Only now, when she grabbed the rolling pin, Sheela took to hiding Suman under the bed and then herself escaping out through the window to stand in the middle of the street, where she was sure her mother wouldn't beat her. The upshot was that Shree remained behind to silently bear the brunt of their mother's wrath.

'When Mummy comes at you with the rolling pin, just run, Shree!' counseled Sheela when she noticed the red welts on her older sister's arms with pity. 'Why do you stand around and allow yourself to get beaten?'

But Shree only looked at Sheela vaguely, not convinced entirely, and returned to reading her book.

6

Jawans are the junior soldiers in the Indian army, below the rank of a commissioned officer. Often hailing from the rural towns and villages, they leave their families behind to live in faraway locations, often thousands of miles away from home, to serve their superior officers and their country.

Bilawal Khan was one such *jawan* designated to the recently-promoted Major Murthy in Udhampur, Jammu & Kashmir. Therefore, in accordance with the rules of the Indian Army, part of his job included helping with the household chores and maintaining his superior officer's uniform in perfect condition at all times. While Bilawal sat in the back garden each evening polishing Major Murthy's boots and leather belt to a high shine, he sang, in his perfect baritone, the Urdu songs that his mother had taught him as a boy. Major Murthy always sat beside him enjoying the music and polishing the girls' black school shoes.

Bilawal was a great favorite with the children. But the softest corner of his heart was reserved for Sheela who won it the day she patted his large belly with her little hand and said innocently, 'Bilawal *bhaiyya*, there is a baby in your tummy. When Mummy's stomach became this big, Suman came out, see? There she is now!' And both of them turned to watch Suman running across the floor in earnest pursuit of an ant. He broke into a hearty laughter with his head thrown back, much to Sheela's amusement, who hardly understood what it was that she had said.

Bilawal had then hoisted Sheela onto his shoulders and taken her out to play. Since then, she had been his favorite, although he was very fond of Shree and Suman too.

A few years went by and Bilawal continued to be an essential part of the Murthy household.

Then, on what seemed like a busy day in the Murthy family, Bilawal helped Indu pack a grand picnic basket. Into it went an assortment of cheese, jam and cucumber sandwiches, bottles of homemade lime juice, freshly fried *masala vadas* and tamarind rice. All of these were Sheela's favorites. She hovered around the supplies a little longer, waiting for her mother to turn her back for a bit so that she could smuggle a treat for Suman and herself. Having accomplished the mission, with some help from the ever-sympathetic Bilawal, Sheela pocketed the contraband and shepherded Suman into the back garden, to enjoy a little mid-morning snack. After all, it tasted all the more delicious after having been nicked from under Mummy's nose! It was 12 October 1970.

Together with other families, that of Major Srinivasan, Captain Saini, Colonel Jamwal and Major Rawat, they all climbed into jeeps and set out for their trip to the beautiful hill station, Patnitop, located some eight miles away. Sheela was overjoyed to have her best-friends-cum-partners-in-crime—the three mischievous sons of Major Rawat—with her! Unmindful of her mother's reprimands, she leaped straight into the Chenab River the moment the jeeps came to a halt, taking all her three friends with her. Major Murthy only just managed to grab on to the tail of six-year-old Suman's frock a moment before she dived in behind her sister. Shree strolled along the banks, humming to herself for a while before settling down with a book. The menfolk pulled out bottles of chilled beer and got down to business, while the women laid out the delicacies and treats from their picnic baskets on the nicely spread out mats. Every family had brought one treat or the other, and several happy hours went by. Sheela could hardly remember a happier day in her life as she swam and splashed around with her friends!

When the children had emerged from the water at long last and wolfed down their lunch, the entire company suddenly broke into the birthday song. Brightly wrapped presents appeared from nowhere and were handed over to Sheela, who stared blankly at them, wondering what was going on. The trouble was that Indu, matter-of-fact as always, had gone to great lengths to organize this birthday gathering for her daughter. Only, she had forgotten to tell Sheela that it was her birthday!

Sheela had turned nine that day.

* * *

One morning, not long after the picnic at Patnitop, Bilawal appeared at the house for his daily chores looking particularly cheerful.

'Why are you so happy today?' Suman asked.

'Because, *gudiya*, my daughter has arrived with her mother this morning!'

Sheela, who was bent over her math sums, looked up.

'Your daughter? I didn't know you had a daughter, Bilawal *bhaiyya*. Where has she come from?'

'From my village. From Haldu Khata,' he said, smiling all over his kindly face.

'Where is Hadlu ... hal ... umm ... Where is that place that you just said?' asked Sheela.

'Haldu Khata.' chuckled Bilawal. 'It's in Uttar Pradesh. Very far from here.'

'What is your daughter's name?'

'Noora Fatima.'

'Noora … How old is she?'

'She is six, *gudiya*. Just like our Suman here.'

'Will you bring her to meet us?' asked Sheela, and Bilawal Khan nodded happily.

In preparation for Noora's arrival that afternoon, Sheela took out her best frock from the cupboard and put it into a paper bag. She hoped that it would fit the little girl. Then she removed the new coloring book and drawing pencils that Major Rawat's family had gifted her on the day of the picnic on Patnitop. They were still wrapped in transparent cellophane, and she put the entire set into the bag along with the frock.

Noora turned out to be a charming child, quiet with beautiful, eloquent eyes. She knew only Urdu, which wasn't a problem because Sheela, Shree and Suman spoke it passably well, it being similar to Hindi. The children liked Noora immediately, and Suman took her around the house to show her the garden and her toys. Noora was thrilled with the gift Sheela gave her and immediately took out the frock and held it against herself. Indu happened to be present in the room at the time and was horrified when she saw the dress! She had saved money for four whole months to be able to afford that frock for Sheela, and to have it gifted away like that! She opened her mouth to protest when her gaze collided with Sheela's. Her daughter was already watching her with defiant eyes. At this, Indu quickly left the room on some pretext, not trusting herself to hold her peace if she stayed behind a minute longer.

By 5 p.m. it had begun to grow dark and Indu switched on some lights around the house. At the flick of the switch, Noora's eyes widened in surprise and her jaw dropped open. Jumping to her feet, she tore through the house and into the bedroom that the three Murthy girls shared.

'*Aapa!*' she cried, using the Urdu term for older sister. '*Aapa!* Come quickly and look!' Grabbing Sheela's hand, she quickly dragged her across the house. Sheela followed hurriedly, curious as to what could have excited the placid child so much!

'What is it?' asked Sheela.

Noora flicked a switch and cried, 'Look, *aapa*! Light! Light!'

Bilawal came to see what the commotion was about, and the rest of the family followed. Then Bilawal said by way of explanation, 'We don't have electricity in Haldu Khata. That's why she is so excited. All this is very new for her.'

Sheela stood there watching Noora, dressed in that frock two sizes too large for her tiny frame, flick the switch on and off in wonderment. Sudden tears sprang to her eyes, and she felt her father's arm go around her. She leaned her head against him.

'She looks very nice in that frock, Sheela,' Major Murthy said, in a voice that reached only her ears. 'It's a good thing you gave it to her.'

It would be another fifty years before the remote Indian village of Haldu Khata, to which Bilawal Khan and his daughter Noora belonged, received electricity.

7

Indu Murthy taught at the army schools at places where her husband was transferred. She taught English to the students at school, and discipline to her daughters at home. Teaching in the same school in which her daughters studied meant that she had them in her class from time to time. It also meant that they received lower scores than the rest of their class in the exam papers that she graded.

'But Mummy, *why?*' asked Sheela, genuinely puzzled. In her hand was her answer sheet in which almost every answer was perfectly worded. Surely, this deserved the highest marks? (In the late '60s, India had not yet come into the alphabetical grade system of assessing academic performance.)

Indu continued to stir the tomatoes in the pan and ignored her daughter's imploring questions. Sheela, who had inherited her mother's determination in full measure, decided that she would not back down. 'I said why did you give me lower marks? Look here, Mummy, look at my answer here and then see the textbook.' Thrusting both under her mother's nose, she said, 'Same answer, see? So now you tell me why you have given me three out of five for it instead of full marks?'

Indu did not look at her but the stirring of the tomatoes grew more vigorous. Her jaw was set and Sheela saw her nostrils flare in righteous indignation. 'So that it would never be said that Indu Murthy was partial to her daughter over the other children in her class,' she muttered through gritted teeth.

'But these scores you've given me are unfair! You don't mind being *unfair* in order to make people think that you are fair?' demanded Sheela.

At these words, Indu turned her head slowly and stared at Sheela in surprise. It was as if what Sheela had said to her was a new thought. She frowned a little and opened her mouth to say something. Sheela held her breath. Was Mummy about to apologize to her? But Mummy never apologized! Not once had she ever heard Mummy say that she was sorry. After a pause that could have lasted a few moments or a few years, Indu closed her mouth and turned back to the stove without a word. Sheela stared at her triumphantly. She had got Mummy to think! She had got Mummy to *almost* apologize to her!

'Well,' thought Sheela, as she went away, 'I suppose an *almost* apology is *almost* as good as a real one!'

* * *

Shree, Sheela and Suman grew up a little terrified of Indu but, like most children, with a sense of great dependence on her. She was the one parent who was constantly there for them, seeing to their everyday needs, shielding them from hunger and the constant sense of deprivation that hovered at their doorstep at all times, even if she could not shield them from her own fluctuating moods. Daddy was lovely; there was no denying that. But as the years went by and the frequency and intensity of the fights between the parents increased, Major H.M.S. Murthy was to be found less and less at home.

Once when Major Murthy's elderly mother came to visit them for a few months, Indu was as uncompromising with her mother-in-law as she had always been with her children. His mother was in her 80s, and suffered from incontinence of the bladder, making an already over-worked Indu's day more difficult. One day, when Indu came home from teaching at school and found a wet patch on the sofa in the living room, her patience snapped.

'What is this nonsense, *Amma?*' she demanded shrilly. 'I have placed a rubber sheet on the chair in your room for you to sit on. Why did you have to come out and mess up the sofa? Who is going to clean it now?'

The old lady looked at her daughter-in-law with frightened eyes. When Indu's voice rose that way, the mother-in-law simply froze. At that moment, Sheela and Suman came rushing into the room to see what the commotion was about. They arrived in time to hear their mother shout, 'I wish both you and your son would be gone from this house! That will be two less people for me to slave after!'

Sheela took in the situation in one glance, grabbed Suman's hand and left. Without a word, she fetched the disinfectant from the bathroom cabinet and began scrubbing the wet patch on the sofa. She followed it with a round of soap and water, blinking back tears as she worked. Suman was unnerved by her sister's troubled face. As she cleaned alongside, she kept glancing at Sheela with big, worried eyes. Suddenly Sheela put an arm around Suman and pulled her close. The girls clung to each other tightly.

That night, when Major Murthy returned home, Sheela climbed onto his knee and said, 'Daddy, why do you let Mummy talk to *Ajji* that way? Why do you let her get so angry with all of us? Sometimes when she becomes aggressive, I get the feeling that it isn't even Mummy in there. It is a monster, someone who really hates us!'

Major Murthy closed his eyes and said nothing for a long time. Sheela didn't know what to make of his silence, and sat looking at him in dumb misery. Finally, her father mumbled, more to himself than to her, 'Each one of us has our roles. I focus on going out to bring in the bread, while the home is her space. She handles everything in here. I don't have the right to question…'

Behind his closed eyes there was a world of pain and frustration at his helplessness to stand up to Indu's willfulness, her volatility. Not because he didn't want to but because he simply did not have the courage. It was simpler, for him, to let things go on their usual way while he himself escaped into the world of card games and whiskey with his friends.

Sheela knew at that moment that her father would never be able to protect his mother or his daughters from Indu's wrath, simply because he had never been able to protect himself from it. Sheela slid off his lap and returned to her room without another word.

8

Just before Sheela turned ten, Major Murthy, in his characteristically generous and thoughtless way, withdrew the money Indu had been saving each month for the children's education and gave it to a friend who was in grave need. When Indu discovered the shortfall in the bank account she shared with her husband, she was livid. There ensued the worst fight that ever took place in the Murthy household.

The girls overheard it from their bedroom, where they sat huddled together. No one dared to come out, not even Sheela, who was the boldest out of the three girls. All Sheela's numbed brain could think at that time was, 'Thank god, *Ajji* is not here. Thank god she has gone back to Bangalore!' Major Murthy's mother had left just the previous week after a six-month-long visit.

The upshot of the quarrel was that Major Murthy left the house. He went to the Officer's Club, his usual refuge, or so they thought. Once things had quieted down in the hall, the girls slowly unfroze, readied themselves for the night and went to bed. 'Daddy will be back in the morning,' said Sheela to herself, over and over again, as she tried to fall asleep.

But when she emerged from her room the next day, her father was not yet home. The girls ate a silent breakfast under the brooding eyes of their grim-faced mother and left for school. When they came

back home that evening, their father still hadn't returned. Nor did
he appear the next day. By this time, Indu was frantic. Nobody had
seen Major Murthy since the night of the quarrel. In fact, nobody
had seen him since the moment he had left the house. For three days
and two nights Major H.M.S. Murthy was missing. On the fourth
day, when he walked in through the front door, he didn't say where
he had been. He never spoke about those three days again, and the
family never asked him. The household settled into an uneasy truce.

* * *

It began with a fever—an unexplained fever with no other symptoms.
If there was one thing that Indu and Major Murthy agreed upon, it
was that the body worked best when left to heal itself. And so, they
interfered as little as possible. Major Murthy did what he was best at
doing—holding his child, keeping her warm and loved. Indu cooked
light, bland meals prepared with little oil, and made sure that Sheela
drank plenty of warm fluids—honey and lime in water, brews made
from the extracts of ginger, pepper, turmeric and holy basil, and the
juice of the Indian gooseberry. Indu had administered all of these
common home remedies to her children quite successfully over the
years, anytime they hadn't been well. She had no doubt that this time
too they would work.

Shree, in her own quiet way, watched over Sheela, reading to her
to make the long hours in bed go by easier. Sheela who had never
been very interested in books slowly found herself being drawn into
the adventures of the Famous Five—the four children and their dog
Timothy—which her big sister read to her each day. As for Suman,
she never left Sheela's side, attaching herself firmly to the ailing girl,
covering her with blankets, spooning meals into her mouth with
affectionate sloppiness and singing her lullabies that kept Sheela
awake more often than they helped her fall asleep!

'Shree?' whispered Sheela urgently on her fourth day in bed. Their youngest sister had been hauled off by Mummy for a bath. 'Could you take Suman out to play for a while? She's driving me crazy!'

Shree laughed and left the room to do as Sheela said. A few minutes later, Sheela heard the child's protests as her older sister shepherded her out the front door with the promise of showing her a new litter of puppies at the end of the street—a non-existent litter, as it turned out!

By the sixth day, just when Indu believed that the fever had run its course and would now start to subside, Sheela's temperature began to rise beyond the 101-degree mark, where it had mostly lingered since its onset. The deterioration was rapid. Within a few hours, it climbed to 105 degrees! The Rawats and the Srinivasans, accompanied by Colonel and Mrs Jamwal, showed up at the Murthy residence that evening and sat them down in the hall.

'Indu*ji*,' began Mrs Rawat mildly. 'It is time to take Sheela to the hospital.'

'Whether you have gone mad, Indu?' demanded Mrs Ambika Srinivasan in her unusual English. Her stout, well-meaning, south Indian heart had little room for diplomacy or patience, particularly in a situation like this. 'You are wanting your daughter to die or whaaat?'

Major Srinivasan opened his mouth to apologize for his wife's directness when Colonel Jamwal interrupted in his slow, grave manner.

'Ambika ma'am is right, Murthy. You cannot hold off treatment any longer.'

'Yes, sir,' mumbled Major Murthy. Colonel Jamwal, as commanding officer of the unit, rarely forced his point. But when he did, his junior officers always obeyed.

'*Chaliye* Indu*ji*, you quickly go and pack the little girl's things,' said the colonel. 'I'm calling the Command Hospital right now. They will prepare a bed for Sheela by the time you take her in. Srinivasan, Rawat, let's go and leave them to it.'

He rose to his feet, and with him the others. With a kindly pat on Major Murthy's shoulder, Colonel Jamwal led the way out. Half an hour later, Indu and Major Murthy quit the house as well, leaving Suman in the charge of thirteen-year-old Shree. Indu carried a small hold-all packed with Sheela's things, and Major Murthy held the dazed child in his arms. Sheela was in pretty bad shape. The fever had taken firm hold and she was restless and agitated. Her body was burning up and even the touch of her father's cool hands cradling her fevered body was agony. She mourned and thrashed without knowing it.

'Can you manage her?' Major Murthy asked his wife, quietly.

Indu's face was set, as it became when there was a difficult task ahead that she was determined to accomplish. 'Of course,' she said, trying to hide her rising panic behind a brisk exterior. She held out her arms, and Major Murthy passed Sheela into them. He placed the suitcase at his feet in the front of his Vespa, and kick-started the scooter. Indu climbed on behind him. She wedged Sheela's body firmly between her husband's and her own for safety, and they rode away.

The chilly breeze against Sheela's burning skin was excruciating. Indu wrapped the shawl she had brought with her firmly around the child, leaving just enough room for her daughter to breathe. At the hospital, a bed was ready for them. The doctors took over, losing no time in starting intravenous therapy and injecting glucose and a combination of drugs.

'Please keep up the cold compress, Mrs Murthy. It will be a while before the medicine starts to work, and in the meantime the fever must not be allowed to go to her brain,' cautioned the doctor, indicating a trolley to one side bearing water in a tray and a clean cloth.

'Is there danger of that happening, doctor?' asked Major Murthy, his voice tremulous.

'I'm afraid so. But we'll keep a close eye on her, Major,' replied the doctor on his way out. Major Murthy turned distraught eyes upon his beloved child, in time to see Indu pull her chair closer to the bed and reach for the towel with a hand that trembled so badly she had to lower it. Unaware of her husband's gaze upon her, Indu paused, closed her eyes for a moment and took a deep breath. When she reached for the cloth a second time, the compress came on and was held in place with a steady hand that never shook or fumbled again. Major Murthy saw all this and took comfort from the intrepid presence of the woman he had loved and hated, fought with and despaired of for seventeen long years.

Husband and wife spent the night taking turns to sponge down Sheela's body. At 2 a.m., as Indu leaned forward to get the cold compress onto Sheela's arms, Major Murthy came up to stand behind his wife. Sheela's eyes, dazed and half-opened, saw her father place a warm shawl about her mother's shoulders, where his hands lingered for a moment. The child smiled then, a faint, tired smile that nobody saw in that darkened hospital room. Turning onto her side, she fell into a deep, peaceful sleep for the first time since her father had disappeared without a trace for those few interminable, excruciating days.

9

When Sheela returned home from the hospital, she was told that the doctors had advised against sending her to school for at least two months. Sheela's pale face lit up for a moment and she smiled. Suman cried, 'Luckeeeeee! Mummy, can I stay home too?'

As Indu bustled about the house preparing Sheela's bed and arranging her medicines on the side table, Suman tailed after her mother whining and begging. She clearly did not see why Sheela should be allowed a hiatus from school when she was expected to attend as usual.

'I'm smaller than she is, aren't I, Mummy? I should be the one allowed to stay at home!' Strangely though, while Indu nudged Suman out of her way as she hurried around trying to fix dinner, she did not smack the child, as she probably would have done in the past.

'You would like to stay at home and do all the housework then, Suman?' asked Daddy, looking down at his youngest with a twinkle in his eye. Completely misreading the irony in his words, Suman looked up at him through her little mop of hair and replied earnestly, 'No, Daddy. I would like to stay at home and sit in bed next to Sheela the whole day and eat all the yummy things Mummy makes for her. Sheela is not well and can't eat too much so I can eat her share too. Just so Mummy won't feel bad.'

Major Murthy burst into a hearty laughter at her innocent response and Sheela let out a guffaw. Even Indu, now readying ingredients for the soup she was preparing in the kitchen, smiled at the little girl's endearing frankness. Only Shree, lost in thought, missed the whole exchange and instead remained standing at the bedroom door watching Sheela with perplexed eyes.

Later she asked, 'You're sure you don't mind staying home for so long?'

'No,' came the prompt reply. 'I don't mind at all!'

'You won't get bored?'

'I'm never bored!' Sheela declared so confidently that Shree shrugged and went away. But she did leave a pile of her favorite books on Sheela's bedside table before she left for school the next day.

Sheela woke up the next morning and found that the family members had already departed to their various callings, leaving breakfast and lunch on the table for her. She ate but the effort exhausted her. So she went back to bed and slept some more. This was the routine that she followed for the next several days; rarely able to leave her bed for long stretches, so weakened was she in the aftermath of her recent illness. The lack of exercise and activity took its toll on her naturally busy mind and body, and within a couple of weeks she slowly sank into depression.

Listless and disinterested, she lay in bed day after day, watching with dim eyes as the family went about its daily business. At first, the parents thought that it was weakness. But after a while, Major Murthy and Indu began to worry that the infection might have taken hold of their daughter again. Terrified at the possibility, they hurried across to the military hospital to consult Sheela's doctor there. Nobody seemed to realize that prolonged inactivity and boredom was affecting their bright, intelligent child. The doctor recommended that Sheela be brought in for further testing the next day, and this drove Sheela to utter despair! The stark hospital room, the endless needles and pain, the smell of disinfectant that clung to her memory as tenaciously as it clung to her nostrils, the ever-present sense of foreboding … again? Would she have to go through all of it again?

Sheela crawled to the far corner of her bed that had been pushed up against the window overlooking the street outside. With her forehead resting against the bars and tears dropping silently into her lap, she watched the people and traffic outside, busy and subsumed by the hustle and bustle of everyday life.

And that is when it struck her.

The world had not stopped just because her life had!

Almost with detached fascination, she thought, 'Look at them out there. Nobody cares! If my being sad means nothing to anyone, then maybe this feeling of mine really does not mean anything at all. What is the point of it? I will never again let myself become so miserable and defeated!'

And so, at the young age of ten, Sheela Murthy learnt a truth that set her on the path to a life that would be unusual and brave—a life fraught with challenges and insurmountable obstacles that she would overcome simply by never letting anything get her down.

When Major Murthy came into her room that night, he found Sheela propped up in bed and reading a Nancy Drew from the pile of books that Shree had left there for her with an uncanny forethought on the day Sheela had come home from the hospital. The dullness in Sheela's eyes had been replaced by a new brightness and fierce determination. The father heaved a sigh of relief and left without making his presence known.

Sheela remained at home for two whole months before she was allowed to go back to school. In that time, she read every book she could lay her hands on—venturing from Nancy Drews to Charles Dickens, Thomas Hardy and other books above her reading age too. She enjoyed the Agatha Christies and Perry Masons in Shree's collection, until she chanced upon *To Kill a Mockingbird*. She read that one from cover to cover in four days flat. She did not understand all of it, especially certain words and cultural nuances of a country thousands of miles away. Some parts she found boring. Nevertheless, the simple truth in the story grabbed her interest and she knew for the first time, as she shut the book, that she would become a lawyer some day and fight to make this a better world.

10

Udhampur, December 1971.

The Murthy family was residing in Jammu & Kashmir when the Indo-Pakistan war broke out.

The British had left India in 1947, arbitrarily dividing the land—the jewel in its crown—into two countries along religious lines. Pakistan, located along the northwestern border of India, was allocated the territory of East Bengal—a Muslim-dominated region like itself. Post-Independence, East Bengal was renamed East Pakistan and it became a non-contiguous province of West Pakistan, geographically separated by a 1,000-mile tract of land. Sharing its borders with Burma (now Myanmar) and the northeastern region of India, East Pakistan was ethnically, linguistically, culturally and ideologically different from the mother country. It writhed under the atrocities committed by West Pakistani troops that had been stationed on its soil. At long last, in 1971, the East Pakistanis decided to fight back.

Mrs Indira Gandhi, the then prime minister of India, took the decision to militarily back East Pakistan's struggle for sovereignty. In December 1971, when Pakistan carried out pre-emptive airstrikes on Indian airbases, India and Pakistan were officially at war.

At that time Sheela and her sisters were studying at Carmel Convent in Udhampur, which had a substantial army presence, as it was on the northwestern border of India.

The girls were in their respective classrooms when for the first time the scream of the air raid siren rent the air like a bad omen. As the sound grew louder with each recurring cycle, all the students in the class clung onto each other, terrified. The hair on the back of Sheela's neck stood on end and the blood in her veins froze. They were all filled with a sense of helpless foreboding, paralyzed with the horrific sounds they had never heard before in their young lives. Miss Shirley, Sheela's class teacher, quickly fought down her own panic so as not let it impede her ability to act swiftly. With a sense of forced calm, she said, 'Girls, stand up and leave the classroom in single file. No need to panic.'

'She's faking it. She's frightened and trying not to show it', was Sheela's first thought. 'Where's Suman?' was her second.

The thirty-one girls from the class were now in the hallway and Miss Shirley hurried to take the lead. 'Come, everyone follow me outside quickly, please. In single file now, remember!'

She marched the girls outside and across the yard to a long line of trenches that had been recently dug up. The school authorities, like many others around Udhampur, had hurriedly prepared these trenches in the evenings after school hours and throughout the night, in anticipation of the enemy air strikes that a recent dispatch from the Indian Ministry of Information and Broadcasting had warned them about. Practically the entire school—students, teachers and support staff—had moved from the school building and into the yard like a river in spate.

'Don't run!' cried one voice, repeatedly, 'Don't panic!' But nobody listened as people tore across the yard in the direction of the trenches.

'Get down into the trenches, and stay down!' called Miss Shirley to her girls. 'Be careful while climbing in.'

The teacher automatically counted them as they descended into the trenches, and that was when she realized that there were only thirty girls present. One from her class was missing.

Sheela!

Miss Shirley spun around and charged back towards the school building, fighting her way through the throngs of people coming at her from the opposite direction.

'Miss Shirley!' cried a voice. The teacher stopped in her tracks and looked in every direction for the source of it.

'Miss Shirley, over here! I'm here!'

Running straight towards her teacher with her little sister in tow, Sheela approached with a big unfathomable smile all over her face.

'Sheela!' gasped Miss Shirley. 'Where did you run away to? Why did you disappear like that, you bad girl!' Through the teacher's indignation, her relief was palpable.

'To get Suman, ma'am! I had to get Suman. I found her Miss Shirley. See? I found her!'

The guileless joy on Sheela's face belied the paralyzing worry she had caused by her disappearance. It belied the existence of war, the politics of hatred, the planes that would fill the skies overhead at any second and rain bombs upon everything, obliterating existence in the flash of an eye. In the middle of that grotesque scenario, here was a child who thought that because she had found her little sister, the danger had passed and there was nothing left to fear.

Miss Shirley stood numb for a heartbeat, not knowing whether to shake Sheela or to hug her. Just then, a colleague who taught physics to the senior school grabbed Miss Shirley's arm as he rushed past, taking the woman and both children with him. They did not stop until they were safely inside the trenches. Almost on cue, the planes appeared as if from nowhere, streaking across the sky and ripping it asunder. The children watched in stupefied terror the aerial light-and-sound show of missiles of hatred, harbingers of death that lit up the sky like the innocuous fireworks on the 4th of July.

11

At first it was all great fun. Any child even remotely connected to a person in the armed forces took it as their birthright to stand around in the corridors or linger in the lunch hall boasting of their military exploits—real and imagined. A second cousin, an uncle once removed, a family friend, a friend of a family friend, anybody would do, as long as you knew him or knew how you knew him, and he was in the army. So, for Sheela and Suman, having Major Murthy for a father ('Their very own papa!' one eleven-year-old was heard gushing in the library) made them celebrities in the school! The two young heroines thoroughly and shamelessly basked in Daddy's reflected glory. Only Shree remained, as always, on the periphery—unaffected as a sleepwalker wandering the world in the cover of the night.

The management decided that since there was no telling how long the hostilities would continue, it would be best to proceed with the original school calendar as if nothing had happened. Thus, half-yearly exams at Carmel Convent commenced on day four of the Indo-Pakistan war.

Since there was the definite possibility of an air raid interrupting the two-hour-long exam session, the school devised a method to mark the time. They now went by the stopwatch instead of the clock.

After her two-month hiatus from school in Delhi, Sheela had returned to academia with renewed vigor, eager to embrace the world and all its challenges. As a result, her grades had improved steadily, until she was a topper of her class; these exams posed no difficulty for her.

She arrived in school with her math book tucked under one arm, exam pad tucked under the other. But at precisely 42 minutes and 14 seconds on the stopwatch, while the 6th graders were in the throes of working out the answers to the sums in the question paper, the now-familiar sound of the air raid siren rang. Remembering to press the pause button, the math teacher, Mrs Gupta, hurried the girls outside.

Gleeful at the unexpected respite, not a single girl of grade 6-B noticed the fireworks overhead. They quickly got the answers for questions four, five, eight, ten, thirteen and nineteen from Sheela, who generously passed them around. Ten minutes later, they were back to their seats in the examination hall and looked suspiciously cheerful as they continued with the exam. This caused Mrs Gupta's internal 'sneakoscope' (or whatever that translated to in the non-*Harry-Potter* world) to light up and spin out of control in her head. She kept a close eye on the girls but not one of them looked up from her answer sheet for the whole of the 77 minutes and 86 seconds that remained on the stopwatch. The air of virtue did not fool the teacher one tiny bit though. And yet, she had not managed to catch them red-handed. So, with a suspicious frown carving the edges of her brows, she watched them troop outside the classroom to the school buses that awaited them after the exam was over.

After serving dinner and clearing away the dishes that night, Mrs Gupta laid the sheaf of answer sheets upon the dining table and began to correct them with her red ink pen. Thirty-one answer sheets with all the same answers. Not unusual. Thirty-one answer sheets with answers to questions four, five, eight, thirteen and nineteen correct.

Not *very* unusual. Thirty-one answer sheets with every single answer to question ten incorrect. *Most* unusual. Thirty-one answer sheets with the *exact same* incorrect answer to question ten. Out-and-out evidence of fraud!

The next day, Mrs Gupta reported to the principal that keeping track of the duration of the exam during an air raid was not the only challenge. The half-yearly examinations in Carmel Convent that year were cancelled.

* * *

Gradually, the enormity of war and its implications began to sink into Sheela. What had at first seemed like a fascinating adventure, now became what it really was—the threat of annihilation to herself, her world and the people she loved. The ordeal lasted thirteen days. Thirteen days and nights of running from classroom to trenches, home to basement. Of earth-shattering explosions caused by bombs that fell in the next street or the one next to it, missing her home, her school by a hair's breadth. Sheela took to waking up in the middle of the night to the imagined scream of an air raid siren. She took to waking up each morning with the thought that this day might be her last on Earth. This might be the day a loved one, a schoolmate or a neighbor simply didn't come home.

As the radios and newspapers reported extensive loss of life, Mrs Gandhi opened up Indian borders in the east to refugees. But the decisive end to nine months of Pakistani civil war came from those thirteen days when India and Pakistan went head-to-head in military combat, simultaneously engaging on land, in the air and at sea.

On one such night, at around 3 a.m., the Murthy residence in Udhamphur quite literally shook from a series of bombs that landed terrifyingly close. Indu charged into the room and dragged her three girls off the bed. The four of them were running towards the trenches outside when Sheela noticed that Daddy wasn't with them.

'Mummy!' she screamed, wresting her hand out of Indu's grasp, 'Daddy isn't here! We have to get him!' She charged back to the house and into her parents' bedroom, where she found her father deeply asleep on the bed. She tried to shake him awake, but to no avail. In desperation, she threw herself on him and began to pummel him. But Major Murthy was too deeply asleep to feel it and instead turned on his side, muttering what sounded like, 'Later.'

Then Indu, who had followed on her daughter's heels, held Sheela from behind and lifted her off the bed. Once Sheela was back on her feet, her mother dragged her away from her sleeping father and towards the front door once again.

'I don't want to leave Daddy!' screamed Sheela. In response, Indu's fingers closed like a manacle over her daughter's wrist. Sheela felt herself being hauled back to the trenches in spite of her best efforts to resist.

Outside, all hell had broken loose. In what seemed like a near stampede, the entire neighborhood was running for the trenches—tripping, falling, jumping back up and shoving each other out of the way—in their attempt to reach for cover before the next bomb dropped.

'Captain Bisht, please help me!' gasped Indu. A second later, Sheela felt herself being inexorably lifted off her feet by a pair of strong male hands, and carried into the trenches, kicking and screaming. Suman and Shree were already in there, huddled close together. Indu followed her second daughter, muttering her thanks to Captain Ranjit Bisht, an officer in her husband's corps. Within seconds, the street was cleared of all life and a minute later an enemy aircraft swopped overhead and dropped a bomb that caused three houses at the head of the street to go up in smoke.

'Daddy is going to die,' thought Sheela, over and over, as the laughing face of her beloved father flashed through her tightly shut eyes. She did not open them to check whether her home had been hit because she could not bear to know. Not yet. Not ever, if she could help it. Instead, she sat there shaking, her arms wrapped tightly around herself, rocking back and forth in agony. All around her, bombs gutted the land.

Just then, a strange muffled sound reached Sheela's ears. Slowly she opened her eyes and turned her head to where her mother was sitting, pressed against her. Was Mummy scared? But Mummy was never scared. And Mummy never cried. Yet there was Indu, leaning forward as she sat with her eyes fixed on the house across the street, desperately willing fate to spare the man inside it; the father of her children, the husband she loved (though may not have known how to show it), who lay asleep and lost to the unkind world around him.

* * *

On 16 December 1971, just thirteen days after the start of the Indo-Pakistan War, Lt-General A.A.K. Niazi of the Pakistan Eastern Command signed the Instrument of Surrender with India. East Pakistan, hereafter to be known to the world as Bangladesh, became a free nation in its own right and was left to stagger slowly back to its feet. The skies over India grew silent again, and gradually life returned to normal.

12

In Puttur, in the southern Indian state of Karnataka, lived a man named Shankar Nayak. A medical doctor by profession, he had been born into the large, once well-to-do family of Narayan Nayak that had been reduced to a state of near-poverty due to its patriarch's habit of unstinting and indiscriminate generosity. When Shankar was fifteen years old, a girl of his own age named Radha Bai, a cousin who had grown up without a father and led a nomadic existence until that time, was invited to come and live in the Nayak household in order to complete her metric examination. With so many children, a horde of extended relatives and a daily stream of visitors, the added presence of one young girl hardly mattered. And so, Radha arrived to live among the Nayaks, making that kindly soil her own and Shankar's family her people.

Radha had lost her father when she was very young and her mother had chosen not to remarry. She had raised Radha, her only child, with what little means she had. One of Radha's aunts was married to the criminal lawyer Vakil Janardhana Rao, who fought to legally abolish the Devadasi system in India. His chief argument, when asked to defend his petition in court, had been that he himself was the son of a Devadasi and so knew better than anyone the evils of the practice.

The Devadasi system stemmed from the tradition of dedicating minor daughters to the temple. These young 'brides of god' were not allowed to marry mortal men. They did, however, eventually end up co-habiting with them in exchange for financial support. In the early days, the Devadasis commanded utmost respect in society, being exceptionally gifted performers of music and dance. As the mistresses of kings and prominent citizens of the town, they wielded great influence in matters of state. But with the consolidation of British rule in India, royal dynasties fell and kings lost their power. The spread of the Christian missionary idea of morality quickly infiltrated an ancient culture in which sex had once been revered as a means to reach salvation.

The standing of the Devadasi in south Indian society plummeted. Therefore, these women were left unprotected and alone in a hostile male world, entirely without a means to earn their livelihood. Many became mistresses of wealthy men, but had no legal claim to his name or to a share in his property after his death, either for themselves or for the children born of that union. Others fell to prostitution to keep food on the table. In order to improve the situation, Devadasi families made a pact among themselves to inter-marry, so that their future generations would be spared the stain and the consequences of illegitimacy.

Shankar Nayak was the progeny of one such marriage. Radha Bai was another.

The blood of strong, pioneering women stirred in Radha Bai's veins. When Shankar left to study at the Madras Medical College, Radha asked to accompany him. She had a deep desire to study and Shankar, the quintessential feminist, took her along and helped her gain admission into the famous QMC, or Queen Mary's College, in the port city of Madras (later renamed Chennai).

When news about Shankar being in love with Radha reached Narayan Nayak back in the village through a self-proclaimed well-wisher, he was overjoyed! He insisted that the couple lose no time in tying the knot. As a result, Shankar and Radha found themselves married—most happily, as it turned out—while Shankar was still a fourth-year medical student.

After completing her bachelor's degree (an achievement in itself for a girl of that era anywhere in the world, let alone in India), Radha went on to teach in a school. Shankar, now a full-fledged doctor, joined the British Indian Army as a medical officer. In 1950, having left the army, Dr Shankar Nayak, Radha Bai and their two little daughters came to live in Puttur, where Shankar was given the position of district health officer.

* * *

Almost as soon as he arrived in Puttur, Shankar realized that the searing heat and constant humidity of the coastal belt of the South Canara district made it an ideal environment for malaria. A man of deep feeling and decisive action, Shankar recognized that something needed to be done quickly in order to alleviate the suffering around him. Losing no time, he handpicked a team of assistants. With them, he set out up the coast of Karnataka, walking through forests and fields in painstaking search of ponds and other stagnant water bodies. Wherever the presence of mosquito larvae was detected, medicated oil was immediately sprayed on the water to cut off oxygen supply and deter further breeding. This operation went on for a few years, until, at long last, Dr Shankar Nayak and his team managed to eliminate the disease from the region.

It would be a full twenty years before the next case of malaria presented itself there again.

* * *

Shankar and Radha had four children—two girls, Sheila and Shanti, followed, after a gap of nine years, by two boys, Vasant and Vijay.

Radha raised her children to respect their father implicitly while she herself engaged in happy, vigorous quarrels with Shankar over any difference of opinion (which happened often enough!). For Radha Bai was a strong-minded, intelligent and fearless woman with a quick temper and an equally good sense of humor. The couple enjoyed their robust disagreements and it was a while before their children understood that the quarrels they frequently witnessed had everything to do with two bright minds coming up against each other and little to do with any ill-will. Indeed, the squabbles only served to bring their parents closer together. They were adversaries, lovers and best friends all in one, and stayed that way for the rest of their lives.

Their third child, Vasant, was a sensitive boy and had a talent for music and visual arts. As he grew into a young man, Radha Bai observed in him an instinctive need for peace and an inability to tolerate the suffering of others; her maternal heart wrapped itself protectively around him.

One evening in the mid-1970s, when the family was living in Bombay, Radha Bai was cooking dinner in her kitchen, which overlooked the back garden. The maid's little son had accompanied his mother to work that day, and from time to time Radha Bai looked up from the stove to watch the child through the kitchen window. He played and talked to himself, building stories in his head and producing sound effects alongside, as he set out on his imaginary horse to fight an imaginary war. It kept Radha Bai amused as she went about her work.

Dusk was fast approaching and winter was upon them—the sudden and brief but sharp winters that always captured the otherwise hot and humid Bombay at that time of the year. She saw the little boy shiver a little, but undeterred he played on. She quickly warmed a glass of milk for him and put out homemade cookies in a tray. Just as she was preparing to take it outside, she saw her seventeen-year-old Vasant emerge from the house. His one and only warm jacket was slung over his arm. Walking across the back garden to where the little boy played, he placed the jacket around the thin young shoulders. The child's head jerked up in surprise and a second later he realized what had just happened and smiled so happily, so gratefully, that Radha Bai found herself blinking back tears.

There would be no jacket for her son that winter, she knew. The family couldn't afford it.

'What will become of him?' Radha Bai asked her husband that night, in the privacy of their bedroom. 'He gives everything away without a thought. And his career ... he is so inclined to the arts that he'll probably create many beautiful things. But will that bring any money with it? How will he survive? I am worried.'

'What is meant to happen will happen,' Shankar Nayak calmly replied in his native Konkani. 'There is no point in fearing it.' This was a phrase he often used and it never failed to reassure his wife. Lulled by his solid presence by her side, Radha Bai fell asleep, never suspecting that the same concern troubled him as much as it did her.

Shankar rarely gave voice to his feelings. But his love for his children was as deep and unyielding as the ocean that washed up against the shores of Bombay, and the diligent care with which he had watched over them since childhood had turned each one of them into a secure and self-possessed young individual. On a fixed salary and with no prospects of an inheritance, Shankar knew he would sell the shirt off his back if it ever came to that, to give Vasant and Vijay the best education they could get. What they did with it later was entirely up to them. He was aware of his limitations, his powerlessness to help should they fail to make it on their own. Vasant, like his paternal grandfather, tended to give away his possessions faster than he could earn them. So yes, Shankar was worried. And while his wife slept that night, he lay awake wondering what the future held in store for their boy.

* * *

While his sons were studying for their bachelor's degrees in the then city of Bombay, Shankar Nayak's work required him to relocate to Hyderabad. The boys stayed on at the St. Xavier's College hostel and completed their degrees—Vasant in sociology with an interest in anthropology and Vijay in commerce. At that time, a Spanish Jesuit priest, Fr John Macia, was Head of the Department of Sociology at the college. He noticed Vasant's keen interest in the visual arts and sent for him to come into his office.

'There is a UGC grant allocated to the sociology department. I'm putting you in charge of it. I want you to venture into rural India and document the lives of tribals. I will arrange for you to be excused from your classes while you are away.' Rising from his chair, he crossed over to the cupboard and removed a beautiful camera that was resting in its box inside. This, he put into a surprised Vasant's hands and said, 'You will need this. The project will last for two months and your expenses will be covered. You leave tomorrow.'

That was the first time Vasant held a camera in his hand. As he gazed at it, a strange joy filled his heart and he sensed, without knowing why, that this was a defining moment, and his life would never be the same again.

* * *

'Can you tell me how far Purushwadi is from here, brother?' asked Vasant as he stepped off the bus at Akole early in the morning—two days after the conversation in Fr Macia's office. He had arrived in a broken-down, intrepid state transport bus whose body parts seemed to be held together by little more than the non-stop prayers of the countless passengers who rode on it. Crowded and bursting at the seams, it should have been retired from service a full decade ago. Instead, it was to be seen careening down the dirt road from Bombay at break-neck pace on any given day!

'Purushwadi? *Do bidi ka rasta, sahib,*' replied the villager, pointing towards the east.

Do bidi ka rasta. The distance one could cover in the time it took to smoke two country cigarettes. That was how far away Purushwadi was. This was not a problem at all! Quickly procuring two *bidi*s from the local shop, Vasant slung his bag over his shoulder and set out on his journey. He lit the first bidi, enjoying the rough heady feel of it. The morning was cool and he felt light and refreshed as the clean, village air brushed against his face. His pace was brisk and he thought to himself, 'People around here probably tend to stroll along. But at my pace, I may even reach before I finish this *bidi*!' Taking it as a challenge, he picked up his pace. When the *bidi* was burning down to its very end, he lit the second one at its tip before stubbing the first one out.

He had still not reached Purushwadi.

He walked on, puffing on the second *bidi*. Maybe the villagers did not walk so slowly after all. Smiling to himself, he switched his bag to the other shoulder and kept going. Soon the *bidi* came to an end, and there was still no sign of Purushwadi. An hour went past, then two hours, and then four. Every time he stopped to ask someone along the way for directions, they pointed towards the east and seemed to have nothing more specific to say. The sun was blazing down from above in a 1 o'clock-in-the-afternoon-sort-of-way, and he stopped to have lunch at a little shack on the roadside. As he sat down at the rickety, three-legged wooden table, he asked the serving boy, 'How much further till Purushwadi?'

'*Bees minut, sahib,*' replied the boy.

That's all? Just twenty minutes? Vasant felt faint with relief, before he realized the boy was still speaking.

'What was that?' he asked quickly.

'I said twenty minutes by vehicle, *sahib*.'

The young man stared at him, aghast!

'And if I were to walk?'

'Oh, that will take two hours or so,' replied the boy cheerfully.

Vasant opened his mouth to say something, but no words came out. He ate in silence. Once the food was all gone (he had to admit it was a very nice meal, having been cooked in an earthen pot over red hot coals), he felt somewhat revived.

'Aren't there any buses from here?' he questioned the serving boy who had returned to collect the empty dishes.

'Oh, no! People travel by bullock cart. You could try to hitch a ride. Where have you come from?'

'From Akole.'

'Akole? You've been walking all the way?'

'Yes. They told me it was *do bidi ka rasta*. But I finished smoking them both in the first twenty minutes and there has been no sign of Purushwadi since.'

The boy looked puzzled. 'In the first *twenty* minutes? You smoked your *bidi*s so quickly?'

The young man frowned. 'Why? How long do you people take to smoke yours?'

'Many hours, *sahib*! They are so expensive, after all. People light them and take two or three puffs, then stub them out, stick them behind their ear for safe-keeping and go about doing their work. A few hours later, they light it again and take a couple more puffs. They do that till the *bidi* is all gone.'

The young man had been walking for six hours now, and it seemed like he still had some distance to cover. His only regret was that there would be no friendly *bidi* to make the rest of the journey easier! Thanking the boy, he paid the bill and went on his way, chuckling ruefully to himself.

13

Colonel Murthy retired from the army and joined Bharat Earth Movers Limited (BEML) on deputation in 1982. The Murthy family relocated to live in an independent house in his hometown, Bangalore. Colonel Murthy's elderly mother Padmavathi had now moved in with them permanently, more out of necessity than choice. This put a strain on Indu and as tempers frayed again the Colonel grew increasingly absent from the dinner table, as his presence at the card table at the Indiranagar Club increased proportionately. This was not surprising though. Being the hearty, affectionate and generous man that he was, his ever-widening friend circle ensured that he was in constant demand everywhere. It was unsurprising also because home was a difficult place for him to be in for more than a few hours at a time. It was not easy to watch Indu lock horns with his mother, and his inability to control or ameliorate the situation left him shaken and disgruntled. His only recourse was to keep away.

With her father away for extended periods of time, the house increasingly ceased to feel like home. And Sheela decided that a hiatus from the claustrophobic environs of an angry and overworked mother, a suffering grandmother and an absentee father would do her good. Madras was not too far away, just 150 miles east of Bangalore, and it was home to the famous Stella Maris College, which she felt would be an ideal place for her to complete her undergraduate studies in history.

'Sheela, what is this?' asked her father, 'Is history really what you're planning to major in?'

'Yes, Daddy,' replied Sheela calmly, raising her eyes from the book she was reading.

'Why?' he asked, looking genuinely puzzled.

'Why not?' questioned his daughter.

'With your grades, your intelligence and your capability, you could easily pick science, become an engineer, or a doctor like Shree. What on earth will you do with a degree in *history*?' he cried.

Sheela looked at her father keenly. He was clearly distressed. 'Daddy, come, sit down,' she said, and he perched himself on the edge of her bed.

'History is interesting,' she explained, 'History repeats itself. There is so much to learn about it and from it. And most importantly, it will help me when the time comes for me to study law.'

Colonel H.M.S. Murthy stared at his daughter for a long time. It was as if he was trying to comprehend something that was proving entirely elusive. How could his precious Sheela—his bright, intelligent darling—end up as a lawyer of all the things! There was something of a stigma attached to the law profession in those days. It was not considered respectable for anybody to get into, least of all a girl from a good, middle-class Brahmin family.

Sheela could see the wheels in Daddy's head turning and figured that he was perhaps visualizing her seated on a rickety wooden desk outside a government office, peddling notarized affidavits to those who came by. She could bet that he was visualizing her in the middle of a bargain with her clients for a decent price. 'No, sir, I will not attach my signature and seal to your document for one rupee less than a hundred! What, you want *two* affidavits to be notarized? Okay then, I'll cut you a deal. One hundred and fifty rupees for two! A real bargain!'

Sheela burst out laughing. Her laughter was so infectious that Colonel Murthy found himself smiling as well, although he didn't quite know why. But when she shared her guess with him, he exploded with mirth, for she had hit the nail right on its head! That was exactly what he had been thinking. How well she knew him!

Once their laughter had subsided, she said earnestly to her father, 'I want to help people who are in trouble and I want to fight injustice, Daddy. A degree in law will help me do that. Remember that book *To Kill a Mockingbird* I used to tell you about? I read it when I was ten and at first I didn't understand all of it. But I've read it many times after that and I have wanted to be a lawyer ever since.'

As she spoke, Colonel Murthy thought about how much she had grown! At sixteen she was nearly as tall as he was and she was attractive, even beautiful. Her eyes danced in a face that was evenly proportioned and when she smiled it was not just with her lips, but with her whole being. Every time she entered a room, it seemed to just light up. The things she was telling him so earnestly just now, the silent appeal for his understanding and his trust that engulfed her explanation, went straight to his heart. Without saying a word, he got to his feet and held out his hand to her. Together they went into the living room where their young maid, Lakshmi, was sweeping the floors. They watched her for a moment before the father spoke.

'Sheela,' he said, 'there is no difference between you and this girl. It is only that you were born in a good home and life has blessed you with better opportunities. Look how hard she works, how diligent she is. You go off and study whatever you like. But when you have succeeded in your career, don't forget this girl and others like her. Make sure that you do whatever you can to help, so that they too can advance in life.'

He spoke softly, so that Lakshmi wouldn't feel as if they were discussing about her in a language she did not understand. Sheela carefully listened to her father's words, letting them sink deep into her.

Words that would remain with her for the rest of her life.

* * *

In 1983 the Colonel's mother passed away. Sheela was distraught at never having had the opportunity to make life easier for her grandmother. Her three years in Stella Maris College had been wonderful—bringing medals and awards, and scoring highest marks in every subject that she undertook to study. And yet, Sheela's heart was not completely at peace. Something kept telling her that she had failed. She loved college and had enjoyed the break from the troubles at home, but a little voice inside her head now whispered that it was time to go back. One could not, after all, run away forever.

And so, at the end of three years, Sheela packed her bags and returned to Bangalore and her old life at the Murthy residence. She brought with her a bachelor's degree, a deep sense of achievement and a certainty that time had finally come for her to make peace with her mother. Despite her anger at being abandoned, Indu was genuinely thrilled to have her daughter back. She showed it by snapping, 'Just because you've been away in the hostel doesn't mean you can flout the house rules!' the minute Sheela walked in through the front door with her suitcases. Sheela grinned, dropped her bags and ran to her mother. She flung her arms around her and when her mother didn't push her away, she knew for certain that Indu was happy to have her back. Suman who had missed her older sister most grievously went into her room and wept.

'What's the matter with you?' demanded Sheela, but Suman only shook her head.

'*Arrey*, tell me,' she insisted in her no-nonsense way.

'When we were kids, every time Mummy and Daddy fought, I used to feel terrified that they would separate and we would be left all alone. But then I knew that you were there and if they did leave, it wouldn't matter because you'd take care of me. Knowing that always made the fear go away. But after you left for Madras, when Mummy and Daddy fought, the fear just stayed and stayed.'

Sheela stared at her younger sister, aghast. As an eighteen-year-old, desperate to get away from the house, she had not once thought how Suman would feel if she left.

'Are you crying because you're sad?' she asked hoarsely.

'No, I'm crying because I'm happy. I'm so happy that you've come back home!'

Sheela pulled Suman into her arms and hugged her tightly, fiercely.

'You have to know that no matter where I am, Suman, I'll always take care of you!'

Sheela instantly recalled her father waiting for her on the platform at the railway station, earlier that day. As she had stepped off the train, he hurried forward and embraced her, and said those exact same words: I'm so happy that you've come back home!'

* * *

The first thing that Professor Coutinho did when he took over as principal of the University Law College (ULC), Bangalore, was to introduce his students to the moot court competitions. He had arrived from Dharwad University where he had trained many students for these competitions and knew their importance. His predecessor had been indifferent to such activities, and consequently, the ULC students had no clue about them. That day, he told them of the All India Moot Court Competition that was to be organized by the Banaras Hindu University.

At that time Sheela was a second-year law student at ULC, and the mention of moot court immediately caught her interest.

Grabbing on to her friend Gayatri's arm, she said excitedly, 'Let's try for this!'

'Are you nuts?' cried Gayatri, aghast, while the others around merely looked at Sheela.

'What for?' asked Shekhar mildly.

'What do you mean what for? For the experience, of course! What kind of lawyers will we make if we don't grab every opportunity to learn and test our skills?'

'*Arrey*, it's already too much to study from our textbooks. Who's going to add to the workload, *yaar*?' grumbled Shekhar placidly, lighting up the cigarette that he had filched from Srinivas' pocket.

'We'll learn on the job, if and when the need arises,' said Gayatri.

'Why wouldn't the need arise, Gayatri?' asked Sheela.

Gayatri shrugged. 'I'll get married once I'm done with college. I may or may not work after that. I'll cross that bridge once I get to it.'

Srinivas and Shekar were already busy wrestling over the stolen cigarette by then, and so Sheela turned away, disappointed.

'I'll go with you.' Pradeep, the quietest member of their group, looked up from his book and said.

Sheela brightened. 'You will? *Really?*'

'If you need me to,' he added.

'Don't you *want* to, though? For yourself, I mean?'

'Not particularly. I'm kind of caught up with becoming a chartered accountant and setting up my CA practice at the moment. But I'll be your team partner if you can't find anybody else.'

Sheela grinned. Grabbing his hand, she pumped it up and down in joy until his spectacles went crooked on his nose. As Sheela ran away to enquire about how to register for this competition, Pradeep called after her: 'You'll have to do most of the work though, I'm warning you. I'll just help with the oral presentation.'

'That's what you think!' yelled back Sheela over her shoulder.

'I really mean it!' he shouted in response, smiling.

14

It turned out that K.R. Pradeep (or KRP) really meant it after all. He truly did not have the time or the inclination to help Sheela with the research or the preparation of the cases for the moot court. She, on the other hand, was like a one-man army—rushing around for the registration, staying up nights to research her case, and prepare the write-ups and presentations. After everything was over, she coached KRP, going over each detail with a fine-toothed comb until he sincerely regretted his decision to involve himself in what he called 'Sheela's Manic Mission'. Nevertheless, he was sharp and grasped the issues very quickly. Having an outsider's perspective, and hence a fresh one, he added strong and novel points that could be used in both the written briefs and during oral arguments. But KRP was not wrong in his summing up of the situation. It really was her mission to win.

And they won.

Third place.

At the All India Moot Court competition held in December 1983, while Sheela was still a second-year law student, she and her partner stood third out of the eighteen law colleges that participated in the event. When they returned to Bangalore with medals in their hands and classmates congratulating them, Sheela calmly said, 'Next year we'll come first.'

She wasn't being boastful. She was just stating what she knew to be her truth. Her seniors had cautioned her against participating when she was only in her second year of law school, saying that she would need the experience of a final-year student to be able to hold her own at a competition as exacting as this one. Well, she had participated and she had won the third place.

'Now we'll have a whole year to prepare for the next one,' she said to KRP.

'*You* will, yes,' he agreed.

In March 1985, Sheela and KRP won first place at the All India Philip Jessup International Law Moot Court competition that was held in Pondicherry, located on the east coast of India beside the Bay of Bengal. Once again, there were over eighteen teams, representing law universities from all over India. From the prize distribution ceremony, bearing the large shield in their hands, they directly made their way to the front desk of the hotel they were staying at and requested the receptionist to place a long-distance call to Prof. Coutinho in Bangalore. While she did so, they counted the money they had between them and put the notes down on the desk to pay for this call, which was going to be very expensive, they knew. When the receptionist had Prof. Coutinho on the line, she handed the phone over to KRP who refused with a shake of his head and pointed to Sheela.

'Tell him!' hissed Sheela.

'No, *you* won. *You* tell him the news,' said KRP and passed the phone to her.

Sheela broke the news to her principal. Prof. Coutinho's heart swelled with pride at the memory of her tireless determination, but he had no appropriate words that could truly express his immense happiness, and so he remained silent. None of the countless students

he had trained at Dharwad University for moot court competitions
had shown the enthusiasm or the commitment to win like the way
this girl had.

* * *

That late March afternoon in 1985 was the fifth one that Sheela
had spent outside the Karnataka Chief Minister's office amidst
tight security, hoping to meet Ramakrishna Hegde, that is, the CM
himself. The CM's personal assistant had noticed the young girl's grit
and determination and ensured that that day she was finally given an
audience. As a result, she found herself sitting face-to-face with the
CM, telling him about the International Jessup Phillip Moot Court
that was to be held in New York City the following month. The state
of Karnataka had never had one of their law colleges win anything
like this, and Mr Hegde did not know what she was talking about
at first. But as she spoke, her clarity and energy proved infectious,
and the CM found himself sitting forward in his chair and listening
closely to her.

'If anybody can win this competition, it would be her,' he thought
to himself, but his face remained impassive.

'What do you want me to do for you, young lady?' he asked,
not unkindly.

'My team partner and I need funding for our trip to the United
States, sir,' she replied promptly, and he found her frankness rather
refreshing. After meeting politicians and sycophants and smooth-
talkers day in and day out, he was glad to see someone who could
get to the point and present her case with the directness that ... what
was her name again?

'What's your name, you said?' he questioned.

'Sheela, sir. Sheela Murthy.'

'Look here, Sheela Murthy,' he said, in his deep-voiced
pragmatic way. 'The Karnataka government will pay for your

travel, your stay, and your basic expenses, but only for the number of days that you will be attending the competition, mind you … food, transport, that sort of thing. Now anything else you want to talk to me about?'

Sheela blinked. It took a moment for it to sink in that she had been granted what she had come for and been dismissed all in the same breath. Relief shot through her. She was going to America! She smiled joyfully and replied, 'No sir, nothing else, except thank you!'

* * *

The electric switches turned on the other way. That was the first thing Sheela noticed when she landed in the United States and reached the Roosevelt hotel in New York. It was a small room that she shared with Pradeep over the next few days. The second was that, unlike in India, there was no water to wash up when one used the facilities. Only toilet paper! Now that would take some getting used to.

As Sheela had packed her bags to leave India in April 1985, Suman who was then studying in a medical college in Pune and happened to be home on a visit, sat on the bed with her legs swinging off the edge and popped roasted peanuts in her mouth while giving her input.

'Pack more socks,' she advised. 'It will be very cold. And how will you manage to wash your underclothes?'

Sheela frowned. 'Why, what's the problem?' She was arranging her toothbrush and toiletries into a travel pouch.

At that precise moment, Mummy walked in with a plate of *murukku*s for the girls to snack on, just in time to overhear Suman hiss, 'A *boy* will be sharing your room!'

'So?' asked Sheela, unperturbed, and Mummy's nostrils flared.

'So, pack plenty of underclothes so you don't have to wash any the whole time you are there, or it will be weird! Otherwise you'll have to dry them right there in the bathroom that you'll be sharing with that Pradeep boy! It will be so embarrassing!'

'Get over it,' said Sheela in her no-nonsense way. 'I'm not bothered, so why should you be?'

Just then, Sheela had bent over her open suitcase to pack her shoes, and so she did not happen to see the light of battle enter Indu's eyes. However, Indu had avoided open confrontation with Sheela ever since she had returned from Madras, partly because she had not failed to notice the new self-confidence that her second daughter exuded, and also because she was afraid Sheela would leave home again if she set her will up against her daughter's too determinedly. However, that day was different. This was a matter of underclothes, and simply could not be passed over so lightly.

In middle-class Indian society in the 1980s, it was not commonplace for men and women who were not married (to each other!) to share sleeping space. But the shoestring budget allocated to Sheela and Pradeep by the Karnataka Government hardly permitted them the luxury of separate rooms at the hotel they had checked into, when they deplaned at the John F. Kennedy airport.

After reaching the Roosevelt Hotel, Sheela placed her suitcase on the stand and began to unpack. And as she did this, her underclothes began to fall out from every nook and cranny. She stared down at them, puzzled. Had she packed all these? *So many*? No, of course not. Mummy! It had to be Mummy! When Sheela removed the legal briefs from their case, she found a bra tucked in between the pages. Casting the garment back into the suitcase in irritation, she counted out the number of pairs that seemed to have found their way in there. One … Two … Three … Five … Ten. *Ten*! And they would only be staying in America for a week. Sheela stole a glance over her shoulder to where KRP was unpacking a similar bag on his side of the room. Luckily, he hadn't noticed the profusion of underwear, or so she thought. Quickly gathering them up, she stuffed the whole lot under the pile of formal wear in one corner of the cupboard shelf, before Pradeep could catch a sight of them. On the other side of the room, Pradeep's lips twitched for a second before falling back into normal lines.

Once they had unpacked, they took turns to freshen up, and got ready to leave for dinner. Sheela had taken out her moccasins from the suitcase and placed them by the door, next to the sneakers that she had worn on the journey from India. As they were leaving, she tried to slip her right foot into the moccasin. But it just wouldn't go in. She frowned at the failed attempts to force her foot in when she realized there was an obstruction. All this while Pradeep was watching her expectantly from the door. Bending down, Sheela picked up her shoe and peered inside it. There was something there. She pulled it out. More underwear! Someone had stuffed extra pairs into her shoes, taking the count up to twelve! She cast one horrified glance at KRP, who could no longer contain himself. He doubled over with laughter and had to hang on to the door to keep himself from toppling over!

Sheela stared at him blankly for a moment, before the irony of the situation hit. She too burst out laughing, thinking, 'Serves Mummy right! She didn't want anyone to see my underwear, and now, thanks to her, that is exactly what happened!'

* * *

A week into the Phillip C. Jessup International Law Moot Court competition, at precisely 2.43 in the afternoon (Eastern Standard Time), Ms Sheela Murthy, fighting off jet lag and a case of overwrought nerves, had the stage. This time too, all eyes in the room were on her. She was faced with a grave-looking panel of judges meant to represent the United Nations International Court of Justice and a room full of law students from all over the world. These students had assumed the role of dueling attorneys for the competition. Standing upon the dais in this daunting room that was supposed to be The Hague, Sheela opened her mouth to speak ... and no words came out!

Pradeep, she, and all the other law students present had argued all morning, as they had been doing over the past week. They had first represented one fictitious country and then the other. ICBAM was the superpower and MIRVA the tiny country looking to acquire nuclear arms to empower itself. At times, the attorneys fought on this side; at other times they fought on the other. Should ICBAM permit MIRVA to acquire nuclear power status at the risk of world peace? Or should MIRVA be denied the right to protect its sovereignty and its borders from foreign aggression? With rigorous practice and lot of back and forth, Sheela had prepared her briefs with some help from KRP, and then argued her stand—first on this side, then on the other. The other teams had six, sometimes eight members—two to research international law and prepare briefs, two to argue for one side and the remaining two to argue against. But Team India had just two people on it who had struggled to get funding for this trip, then struggled to reach America on a shoestring budget and now struggled to ready themselves for the actual battle.

For two hours, Sheela represented ICBAM. Then, after a fifteen-minute break, she found herself arguing MIRVA's case. Then she had to switch back to ICBAM, and so on and so forth. That was the way the competition played out. At last, at 2.43 p.m., as Sheela mounted the dais on the final day to make her closing arguments, her mind just went blank. She could not remember which side she was on! ICBAM? MIRVA? She fought down the panic as one part of her brain screamed, 'I've lost! I am going to make a fool of myself right here!' while another part cautioned, 'Relax. Calm down. Or for heaven's sake, at least pretend to be calm.'

She glanced across the room, starting from her right, scanning, until her eyes came to rest on Pradeep's face; he was seated at the table to her left. She saw him blink, as if in slow motion, and something in his eyes conveyed a sense of recognition, of knowledge. He knew she was in trouble. Her eyes held his for one desperate moment, and then slowly he smiled and nodded imperceptibly, assuring her that all would be fine. The air left her lungs in a rush, blood resumed movement in her veins and she knew it would be okay after all. Turning back to face the judges, she realized that someone was asking her a question.

'Ms Murthy, you know well that if your country acquires nuclear weapons, every other nation in the world will press its right to be allowed to do the same. And yet, you have no objection in plunging the world into a deadly arms race?'

MIRVA. This question meant that she was now representing MIRVA.

Taking a deep breath, Sheela raised her chin and looked the questioner directly in the eye. In a clear, confident voice she responded, 'Sir, ICBAM was once a nation that used bows and arrows and tomahawks to protect itself. And we all know how that ended for its people. The citizens of MIRVA would prefer not to find themselves in a similar position. When those who took over ICBAM first ventured into acquiring nuclear weapons, I believe they did not pause to think that *they* were plunging the world into a deadly arms race. And by doing so, they set precedence. MIRVA is merely asking to be allowed to follow that precedence.' Sheela smiled her full, disarming smile and added lightly, 'After all, imitation, as they say, is the best form of flattery!'

There was one moment of silence, and then the room erupted into applause, getting to its feet as one. Sheela looked around, a sense of wonder coming over her that she had pulled it off despite the odds. That she had said what she just said. That she had not let her country down, after all!

Sheela and KRP returned to India having won second place at the Jessup International Law Moot Court competition for their written memorials. Sheela Murthy was awarded the Third Best Individual Oralist in the International Division of the Moot Courts. On their journey home, KRP was happy. He kept beaming at his dynamic partner, he was clearly so proud of her. She, on the other hand, kept glancing at him curiously, wondering how he could have attended the world's most prestigious law competition and remained so detached from the whole process. Why hadn't he tried harder? Why hadn't he tried at all? It wasn't as if he was lazy. He worked hard at anything he truly cared about. So why not at this?

'Why did you join law school, Pradeep?' she asked him suddenly, some 43,000 feet above the Atlantic. KRP turned to her and replied, 'It came with subsidized housing in the university dorms. I needed a place to stay.'

15

Shanti, Dr Shankar Nayak's second daughter, had married and settled in Baltimore. In the early 1980s, she invited her parents and her older sister, Sheila, to visit the United States. But Sheila had been observing her brothers for a while.

Vijay appeared to be doing okay, while Vasant did not quite appear so. Sheila had a deep, almost maternal love for Vasant, and watched over him fiercely from afar. She feared that the refinement of his naturally sensitive nature would not withstand the current state of things. He preferred solitude, tended to suffer in silence and was clearly adrift where his career was concerned. Having completed college, it was obvious that his heart lay in photography. But whoever earned enough to get by on just from taking photographs? It was the era of doctors and engineers.

Moreover, Vasant was obsessed with philosophical works of Camus, Huxley and Hemingway. Engrossing himself in such literature only seemed to drive him more deeply towards the pursuit of knowledge and the spiritual essence of things. He read for long hours, any book that he could lay his hands on, and practiced percussion until he seemed to lose consciousness of the world. He even remained oblivious to the squalor of his living conditions in Bombay, where he earned almost nothing for the work he did, and often did not have enough food to keep his body and soul together.

The parents were worried too. Many young women, who came by Vasant with his deep, soulful eyes and long hair, found him attractive. What if he made an unsuitable match with someone who would take advantage of his goodness? Or worse still, what if he never married at all? Marriage, they felt, was one sure shot way for their child to settle down in a more steady life. In this belief, they were heartily joined by just about every set of parents in India!

'At least we know that no girl will try to marry him for his money!' Shankar said one day, and Radha shook her head ruefully over the circumstances of her darling, penniless boy. So, when the time came for Sheila to accompany her parents to the United States, she asked if Vasant could be allowed to take her place instead.

Shankar and Radha arrived with their son in Baltimore city in the summer of 1983. Vasant carried with him nothing except a knapsack that contained two pairs of jeans, two t-shirts and a portfolio of the photographs he had taken over the years—the last thing he had put into his knapsack on an impulse (although what earthly good it would do him so far away from home he couldn't imagine!)

The Nayaks stayed in America for a month. Vasant made the most of this time by thoroughly exploring his surroundings on foot, often recalling his endless walk to Purushwadi on that day, long ago. The landscape, the foliage, the people of Baltimore were so different that it seemed almost impossible to believe that in a faraway corner of the world, under the same sun that shone over America, existed the village of Purushwadi and its people. He thought of dusty dirt roads, sunrises over green fields through which he had tramped during his days of the tribal project, the rough taste of *bidis* that lingered in his memory ... he knew that his heart had been left behind there somewhere. Yet, he was grateful for this opportunity to visit a new country, especially one as vast and welcoming as America seemed to be. He was grateful to Shanti and her husband for making it happen.

The campus of the University of Maryland, Baltimore County (UMBC), was not too far from Shanti's home. Vasant felt oddly drawn to it every time he walked in its vicinity. It was as if something in his destiny was calling out to him. One day, he mustered up the courage to enter the campus gate, portfolio in hand.

It was a turning point in his life.

On the very first visit to the campus, Vasant met a professor, Jerry Stephanie, who was a student of the great guru of photography, Minor White. White's work had long captured Vasant's admiration. Jerry took to him so instinctively and completely that Vasant found himself admitted to UMBC with a full scholarship towards a bachelor's degree program in the spring semester of 1984. Jerry Stephanie remarked, after reviewing his photography portfolio, that there is not much that Vasant could learn at UMBC, because his knowledge had already gone beyond what the program could offer him. He suggested that Vasant would do better to invest his time at UMBC in researching the works of world famous photographers that were in the university archives. Shankar and Radha, more relieved and grateful than they could express, returned to India with their son. Thereafter, Vasant applied for the F-1 student visa to be able to return to UMBC to seriously pursue his education in photography.

The spring semester of 1984 went by quickly, and the learning was tremendous and intensive. Frugality was an art that Vasant had mastered very early in life. Certainly, being a poor student in America brought many more creature comforts than being a poor student in Bombay did. But it was more than that. It was learning to live in an alien country, with a way of life that was so different from his own. It was exquisitely painful and unbearably exciting at the same time. When the semester was over, he was informed of a

couple of prestigious scholarships that had been granted to him for
two one-week-long photography workshops on the west coast, to be
conducted in the summer of 1984. These scholarships were at the
Ansel Adams Gallery in Yosemite, and at the Friends of Photography
in Carmel. The essence of photography was revealed to him at these
workshops. It was a life-altering experience for Vasant.

* * *

The Indian Institute of Hotel Management (IIHM), Bangalore,
was looking for a replacement for their old professor of Travel and
Restaurant Law, who had left them abruptly halfway through the
academic year. Having heard about the young, dynamic final-year
law student's thumping success at the Jessup International Law Moot
Court competition from a colleague at the University Law College,
the vice principal of IIHM, Mr Saxena, approached Sheela Murthy.

'Me? Teach a course at IIHM?' she cried incredulously. 'But I
haven't even graduated yet!'

Unschooled in the social niceties of the working world, Sheela's
candid outburst only served to impress Mr Saxena more.

'You'll do,' he said with an amused smile. 'We don't mind if you
don't mind. Do you?'

Sheela stared at him, still too taken aback to respond. But he was
looking at her steadily, and respond she would have to.

'Er … no. No, sir, I don't … that is *yes* … I can teach at IIHM!'
What began as a stutter ended in confident acceptance of a job that
she suddenly knew in her heart she would be able to do, and do well.
So, she joined as a teacher of Travel and Restaurant Law. When the
management discovered that she had studied four years of French at
the Alliance Française and was now studying Business French there,
while also teaching French to beginners, they pressed her to take on
the additional role of a French teacher at IIHM. This left her no time
to breathe. Between law school, teaching and the hours she spent

at the Alliance Française, she was busy—busier than she had ever been—and loving it!

* * *

The young man had thoroughly enjoyed his two weeks of immersion in photography in California. After that, he completed another semester at UMBC, before packing his bags to return to India. He had made friends both in California and at UMBC that he knew he would keep for life. The faculty at UMBC, at the workshops, as well as the students who had attended the workshops alongside him, were very sorry to see him go. But Vasant was practical. There was nothing left for him in America, and living with his sister and brother-in-law with no job or purpose was simply unacceptable to his pride and sense of decency. The truth was that he was confused. His heart was in India. But back home, the education at UMBC and the workshops in photography would carry no weight in terms of earning a livelihood. He was not certain how many opportunities for meaningful creative work they would bring him either. Employment he would find—mundane work to bring food to the table. Even if he did not find any work, he would starve, and that prospect held little fear for him. It wouldn't be the first time, and he would do it again if he had to. The only sadness lay in the knowledge that the future that awaited him back home was a job in which his heart may never lie.

Bidding goodbye to his friends and family, and to a country he had come to value for its generosity and inclusiveness, Vasant returned to India.

Shankar and Radha took one look at their son when he stepped off the plane and knew that he had returned home with more than he had taken from it when he had left. He had gained formidable knowledge in photography now, and had his own camera. The gauntness had left his face, and there was an air of quiet confidence that had been heretofore missing from his silent, unassuming nature.

Returning to life in India turned out to be easier than he had expected. In time, Vasant found people who shared his passion for photography. Impressed by his work, and particularly by the spiritual undertones of his black-and-whites, they frequently invited him to participate in exhibitions that were being conducted in different parts of the country. His best work eventually found its way into prestigious galleries like the Jehangir Art Gallery in Fort, Bombay. Very soon, he had another exhibition coming up at the Alliance Française, Bangalore. It was a quaint place, nestled into a quiet pocket of an otherwise bustling area, and people of good art sensibilities could be found wandering about the gallery, closely examining the exhibits displayed there. The young man keenly looked forward to seeing his own black-and-whites on those walls.

Shortly before his exhibition dates, a letter had arrived. It was addressed to Vasant and carried on it a return address that read: Purdue University, West Lafayette, Indiana.

* * *

The Alliance Française, Bangalore, was Sheela's second home. She knew every nook and cranny of it, and made it her business to know everyone who ever worked or studied there.

'Don't be so nosy,' scolded the librarian, although she secretly enjoyed watching strangers jump in alarm every time Sheela marched up to them and demanded that they state their business.

'You wouldn't let strangers wander over *your* backyard, would you?' retorted Sheela indignantly, and the librarian grinned in defeat. The fact was that after Sheela had got her answer, she would smile her warm, lovely smile and proceed to show those strangers around or help them find whatever it was they had come looking for. The librarian knew this, as did everyone around there, which was why no one ever took her words amiss!

One evening, when her Business French lesson came to an end and she was gathering her things in preparation to go home, her teacher stopped her at the door.

'There is a photography exhibit going on below. If you hurry you just might catch it. It's quite amazing, you really shouldn't miss it.'

'Okay!' called Sheela over her shoulder and quickened her pace. She made her way straight to the gallery and found that the visitors had departed. All that was left were the cartons on the floor, into which two men were carefully lowering the last of the exhibits. The walls were bare; the exhibition was over.

Feeling strangely disappointed, Sheela wandered across to the library to have a word with her friend before leaving for home. And that's when she saw him. A young man with hair that reached down to his shoulders, lounging in the chair opposite the librarian. Hurrying inside, Sheela came up behind them. The librarian saw her first and her eyes widened in alarm. But before she could stop her, Sheela demanded of the young man, 'Who are you? What are you doing here? It's closing time, don't you know?'

The young man turned his head around and looked up at her in silence. The deep, soulful eyes held her fiery ones steadily, and Sheela held her breath for a moment. There they remained, the three of them, as if frozen in a cinematic frame. Unhurriedly, the young man got to his feet and extended his hand to Sheela.

'Vasant,' he said. 'Vasant Nayak. I'm here for the photography exhibition.'

16

Sheela took Vasant's hand and forgot to shake it. She had had fleeting crushes on guys in the past, very few and far between. But none had ever affected her this powerfully before. Her numbed brain told her that her hand had been in his for a while now. She should let go. Decent girls in India did not maintain lengthy physical contact with a man they had just met, it wasn't considered right.

She turned her head slowly and looked at her friend, the librarian, who was watching them with her mouth slightly open. Vasant's eyes remained fixed on Sheela's pretty, expressive face, and when she turned back to him she saw amusement stir in their depths. So he knew what she was thinking! Well, let him. She liked him, liked the feel of his hand in hers. Who cared about propriety? She would not be the first to let go!

'I heard wonderful things about your photographs. My professor told me about them and I came as soon as my class got over. But when I reached the gallery, the photos had been taken down. I guess I was too late.'

'Would you like to see them now?' he asked.

Sheela's face lit up, and Vasant knew at that moment that he would cheerfully open every single one of the six cartons he had painstakingly packed just minutes ago to show her the photographs in them if she asked him to!

Sheela and Vasant left the library, entirely forgetting to say goodbye to the librarian, who watched their retreating backs in amusement. 'Thank god they at least stopped holding hands,' she chuckled to herself, as she replaced books on the shelves.

Making their way outside, Vasant led the way to the gallery.

'Ajit!' he called to one of the two men Sheela had encountered packing the photographs. The man rose from where he was bending over a carton and walked across to join them.

'This is Sheela Murthy. Sheela, my friend Ajit.'

Ajit was charmed. Like Vasant, he offered to unpack a few of the photographs to show her, but Sheela protested. 'Please don't! It's not fair on you guys. If there are any photographs that you haven't yet packed, you can show those to me.'

It just so happened that there were three or four frames piled up on the side waiting to be put away, and Sheela was thrilled with what she saw. There was soul there, a larger-than-life-quality that came across not through size but through perspective and subject. One knew, at once, that the eye behind the lens recognized his own insignificance in the face of a world that was vastly powerful. She blinked back tears, and Vasant's expression, as he gazed at her, softened.

After that, they headed to a coffee shop, where the three of them chatted like old friends. As she answered their questions about her work, Sheela put away four samosas, smacking her lips unabashedly in enjoyment. That is how it was with her—she was incapable of doing things in half measure, and that included eating samosas! Both young men were refreshed by their encounter with this guileless, happy-hearted girl, who said what she thought and almost always had something meaningful to say. There was nothing coy about her and yet she was unselfconsciously attractive. Unaware of the impressions they had formed of her, Sheela looked at her watch and declared that it was time to go home.

'Come to my place, tomorrow? Come for lunch. I live in Indiranagar. Mummy makes the world's best *parathas*!'

Telling himself that the *parathas* were the real attraction, Vasant, with Ajit in tow, landed up at Sheela's place at 1 p.m., the next afternoon. Indu, who loved to cook and loved it when people loved her cooking, had outdone herself. She had made three different kinds of *parathas*—*aloo*, *gobi* and *paneer*—and a host of other dishes as well. Even the pickle she served was homemade! The fact of the matter was that she had seen the sparkle in her daughter's eyes as Sheela had spoken of this photographer chap that she had met the previous evening. Someone called Vineet … no, Vasant … and Indu was keen to meet him and see for herself what he was like. She said nothing to Colonel Murthy for the fear that he would spread the word among his friends in his usual, unreserved way, and scare away what might turn out to be good fortune. So, the Colonel who was not at home on the day the two young men came to lunch remained none the wiser.

Lunch that day was a pleasant meal, and there was more talk about work and careers. 'I leave to begin a master's program at Purdue University next month,' Vasant informed them in between bites, and Sheela's heart sank. He was going away, then. And so soon!

She didn't know it, but her disappointment was written all over her face as she exclaimed with some effort, 'That's great, Vasant! It's terrific that you got into such a good university!'

'He didn't get in,' mumbled Ajit through a mouthful of food. 'He was *invited* in.' 'What do you mean, invited?' asked Indu, puzzled.

'He attended a summer workshop in California and then returned to India. But the people at the workshop—some of the students and professors he had interacted with while he was there—they really took a liking to him and felt that he should pursue his formidable talent. So they arranged for his admission and financial aid without telling him. The University sent him his acceptance letter last week!' Ajit was clearly proud of his friend.

Sheela grinned because, despite her disappointment over Vasant's impending departure, she was thrilled by this story! And Indu, without knowing how it happened, warmed to the self-effacing young man quite completely, and in a way that was unusual for her.

Suddenly, Vasant looked up and said, 'You should apply to Harvard, Sheela. You'll get in.'

Sheela frowned. What was he talking about? *Harvard*?

'Why would Harvard want someone like me?' she asked, bemused by his suggestion.

'Why wouldn't they?' asked Vasant. 'You've been a topper right through, you have a law degree from one of the best law colleges in India, you already have work experience, and that too work that is related to your field of study. Very few people can claim to have that while studying in this country, you know? Most importantly, you won at the international moot court competition.'

Sheela's head jerked up. 'How did you know?' she demanded, glancing at her mother accusingly. But poor Indu looked as surprised as she was. Vasant smiled and pointed to the shields in the showcase. 'Those would carry considerable weight with a law school like Harvard, you know?' he said.

Sheela was silent for a moment. She was thinking about what a classmate of hers, who had applied to law schools in the US, had told her about the application process.

'I was told that the application fee alone can kill you,' mumbled Sheela at last.

* * *

Now that the photography exhibition was over, Vasant had no excuse to remain in Bangalore any longer. His parents were visiting their eldest daughter in Madras, and he left the next day to join them.

It was written quite plainly on Vasant's face that something momentous had happened. The Nayaks were a close-knit family, and when his sister Sheila questioned Vasant, he told her at once about the girl (her namesake!) he had met in Bangalore. He quite readily confessed to being interested in her. His mother and sister were overjoyed! Dr Shankar Nayak, true to his stoic nature, had little to say. Brimming with questions, the womenfolk extracted all the information Shankar would have wanted to know from Vasant about Sheela. So, all that the father had to do was listen. Then, saying that he had work to attend to, he left town that same night.

Colonel Murthy was sipping his coffee in the front garden of his Indiranagar bungalow the next morning when a stocky, dark gentleman with a strong face, salt-and-pepper hair and thick-framed spectacles perched upon a prominent nose arrived at the gate. He had with him a small overnight bag.

'Excuse me,' the gentleman said in chaste Kannada that carried the unmistakable accent of the coastal belt. 'I am looking for Ms Sheela Murthy. Have I come to the right place?'

Delighted to have a caller so early in the day, yet taken aback that it was for his daughter, Colonel Murthy received him with his customary warmth and enthusiasm.

'I am Colonel Murthy, Sheela's father. Are you a professor of hers from law school, sir?'

'I am Dr Shankar Nayak, the father of a friend of hers. I have come to meet her. Forgive me for intruding this early in the day. I have only just arrived from Madras by the night train that brought me into Bangalore early this morning.'

Colonel Murthy invited him inside at once. When news reached Sheela upstairs that Vasant's father had come to meet her (Indu sent urgent word with the maid), she hurried down to receive him. For a moment, she thought that she heard Vasant's voice and her heart missed a beat. Then, hearing a slightly different accent, she realized it must be Vasant's father. There was no doubt in her mind what this meeting signified, and she welcomed it. Indu met her at the bottom of the stairs looking excited.

'What will Daddy think?' asked Sheela worriedly.

'Nothing, since we haven't told him about Vasant's existence at all,' whispered Indu.

'Poor thing, he's going to be so puzzled. Maybe we should have told him before something like this happened!'

'No, it's better this way. Daddy can't keep a secret; you know how he is. It would have been all over the Indiranagar Club by now had we told him about Vasant's visit!' said Indu. 'Now act natural.' Suddenly she looked Sheela up and down and exclaimed, 'Oh my god, you're in your night suit! Couldn't you have changed before coming down, you silly girl! Go back up and wear something more traditional, go!'

'No,' said Sheela firmly. 'Why should I pretend to be something I'm not? Let Vasant's father see me for what I am.'

There was no time to argue and no space either—the men were in the next room and every word the mother and daughter exchanged carried with it the risk of being overheard. Arguing over something then would simply not end well, Indu decided, and so she gave in. The two women entered the living room together. Sheela came right up to Dr Nayak, folded her hands in greeting, and smiled. Shankar Nayak looked up at her from the sofa. His face was sober, but his eyes had a merry twinkle in them.

'I heard so much about you, I thought I would drop in for a few minutes and visit you in person while I was in Bangalore.'

'I am so glad you did! Thank you for coming,' replied Sheela heartily, taking a liking to the gentleman at once. She had nothing to go by; Vasant had not had the chance to tell her much about his family in those two meetings. But she had a feeling that Shankar Nayak was somebody she could grow to like very much.

'You've arrived from Madras, you said, doctor?' asked Colonel Murthy.

'That is correct.'

'And where do you go from here?'

'Back to Madras for a few days before I return to Mangaluru,' came the reply. 'That is where I am posted currently.'

'Aah, I see. Then you must stay with us while you are in Bangalore,' said Colonel Murthy heartily.

'Oh no, thank you. I return by the afternoon train,' replied Shankar Nayak, before realizing that he might have let on too much about his true purpose for coming to this city.

'So soon!' exclaimed Colonel Murthy. 'What work could you possibly have that would get over so qui—'

'Let me get you something to eat,' cut in Sheela quickly, and despite Shankar Nayak's protests, both mother and daughter whisked him away to the dining table where they set out plates for *idlis* and chutney. In the meantime, the elderly doctor washed and refreshed himself before joining them at the table, where Sheela served breakfast and made him comfortable. He observed her the whole time and saw how she watched out for people, filled their plates, fetched and carried, the kindness with which she addressed the servants, and yet did it all without self-consciousness or the intention to impress.

'Vasant has chosen well,' thought the elderly doctor. 'They will take care of each other.' And, for the first time in many years, he knew a sense of deep relief, a lifting of a burden he had carried inside him without quite knowing it.

'Your daughter is a friend of Sheela's from Stella Maris College?' asked Colonel Murthy innocently. Momentarily distracted from his thoughts, Shankar Nayak hesitated. It wasn't his place to correct the Colonel's misconception and disclose the truth, he felt. The girl would do it in her own good time. 'Yes,' he replied, 'they are good friends.'

Rising from the table, he declared that it was time for him to go. He thanked the family for their kind hospitality and took their leave. Sheela accompanied him to the gate, where he pressed a 100-rupee note into her hand as a blessing, a gesture of acceptance of her into his family. With that, he left the house.

* * *

Within a week of his departure for the US, Sheela had a letter from Vasant. She wrote back a long reply, sharing with him the details of her life and her daily routine. She also shared with him her thoughts and ideas, and he wrote back at length. Soon, a letter from Vasant became the highlight of her week.

One afternoon, a few weeks after he had left the country, there was another letter from him. This time it was enclosed in a large envelope that contained a smaller one inside. Sheela checked the contents. The smaller envelope was from Harvard Law School. In it there was an application form, accompanied by a note from Vasant that read:

'Don't bother applying to any other college. Only go for the best. You lose nothing by trying. P.S. The application fee for this one has been paid.'

17

'Sheela here. All quiet around the science building,' she said into her walkie talkie.

'Roger,' came the response from the law-enforcement officer at the Harvard Command Center.

'Er ... no, this is Sheela,' she corrected.

'Roger,' he repeated.

'*Shee-laa*,' she tried again, enunciating like she would have for a child.

'Ro-*ger*!' replied the officer, irritably.

'Oh, I see!' thought Sheela. 'He's telling me his name. How silly of me!'

'Thank you, Roger,' she said pleasantly and hung up on a very puzzled officer.

In her first few weeks at Harvard Law School, while working as a student campus security officer, Sheela would meet many Rogers before she caught on to the fact that the word was jargon for 'message received and understood.'

'It wasn't someone's name, after all!' she told Vasant seriously on his first visit from Purdue. 'And here I kept thinking that the Americans had no imagination at all, and that's why so many of their kids were named Roger! It was only when a girl used that term that I realized something was wrong!' Vasant stared at her for a moment, his lips twitching, then pulled her close and hugged her. He still couldn't believe that she was here in the United States with him, instead of far away in India!

He visited often after that, whenever he could manage the expense and she could take the time out of her overwhelming schedule. She worked forty hours a week as a student campus security officer, and pulled many an all-nighter trying to keep up with the grueling workload that an LLM degree from Harvard Law School demanded. The Socratic method of analyzing and discussing that was adopted at Harvard was a far cry for the rote learning of the Indian curricula she had grown up with. It delighted her to put her bright, argumentative mind to work in this fashion, but it also called for a formidable amount of hard work. The students in her class might appear at lectures casually dressed and chewing gum. They might sit with their feet propped up on the desk while listening to professors as they taught (a phenomenon that was literally unheard of back home in Indian classrooms!). But they were not casual about anything else. They were students from top law colleges around the world, the brightest minds that one could come by, driven with ambition and purpose. Sheela enjoyed every minute of it!

Sheela's heart belonged to Daddy. He was still the love of her life. But with the passing of years, she had come to recognize that her skills at operating in this world had been nurtured and honed by her mother. Strict and difficult though Indu's upbringing had been, it had made Sheela, Suman and Shree the high achievers that they had become today. Shree was an obstetrician & gynecologist now, Suman was specializing in ophthalmology, and here she was, Sheela Murthy, well on her way to earning her master's degree in law from what was arguably the most reputed law school in the world. Vasant had pointed this out one day when she had complained to him about the manner in which her mother bullied Daddy.

'She's so *strict*, she objects to his playing cards with his friends. He's a grown man, an *old* man, nearly! Surely these are decisions he can make on his own?'

At that point Vasant had asked, 'Had you been in your mother's place, Sheelu, had you been Colonel Murthy's wife instead of his daughter, would you have behaved differently from your mother?'

Sheela had stopped speaking and stared at him. She had remained pensive for the rest of the day, and Vasant had left her alone because he knew that she was thinking. It was something she would need to work out for herself in order to make peace with her mother, in her own heart at least. 'The sooner,' Vasant thought, 'the better.'

* * *

At Harvard, Sheela studied international law, human rights, business and taxation. She graduated with honours with a *Latin Legum Magister*, in other words a master of laws degree, in the summer of 1987. Simultaneously, Vasant completed grad school at Purdue.

The first thing the couple did after that was to get married.

They tied the knot at the courthouse in Ellicot City, Maryland. The only family in attendance was Shanti, who was the official witness at the event. Utterly broke and too happy to care, the newly-weds bought a car with the dregs of their savings and took a road trip around the country. This was the honeymoon or, at any rate, their version of it!

Sheela had a job waiting for her at a prestigious New York City-based law firm. Being a Harvard graduate, no less was expected of her, and she threw herself into her work—body and soul. As it turned out, the law firm, like most large ones of its kind, paid its employees to expend blood, sweat and tears in copious quantities. What happened to the soul in the process was collateral damage.

Ensconced in a small apartment from whose window the firm's building was visible, equipped with a smattering of furniture they hurriedly purchased from IKEA in the course of a single shopping expedition, Sheela and Vasant settled down to married life. Sheela soon found that she was not quite considered human by her bosses. She was a machine that was put to work fourteen to eighteen hours a day, so that the clients could be billed for it. There was hardly any direct human interaction with the client, and little occasion to exercise compassion or concern. In the meantime, Vasant worked as a researcher for a big photo stock agency, and later as an assistant to a commercial photographer. At long last, on the verge of a burnout, Sheela stopped one day and looked at herself in the mirror. At this rate, she would be financially comfortable, possibly 'rich', compared to how she had grown up. 'Only,' she thought, 'I will be rich and soulless. Is this why I became a lawyer?'

Suddenly, the memory of Daddy imagining her sitting outside a government office on a rickety wooden chair, peddling affidavits to all who passed by sprang to her mind. Only this time, the memory did not make her laugh. 'What I am doing now is nearly as bad as what Daddy had feared I would end up doing. This job has no connection with helping people or fighting injustice. It has nothing to do with why I became a lawyer.'

The next day, Sheela went in to work and quit.

Soon after, Sheela and Vasant moved to Baltimore, where Sheela was offered a job at a law firm, and Vasant the position of photography instructor at the prestigious Maryland Institute, College of Art (MICA). Getting a foot in the door, teaching at such a reputed institution was not easy. But the college offered extension programs—evening and weekend classes for different categories of students, including those who were not in the usual age bracket—and Vasant began by teaching those. Gradually, he became part-time faculty. Not long after, his skill at his craft and his considerable talent for teaching resulted in the post of full professor. At that point he went on to design and direct a master's program in digital art and photography. The course was one of the first of its kind in the world.

On the other hand, Sheela became the celebrated new employee of a corporate real estate law firm called Gordon Feinblatt, who couldn't believe their good luck in landing a Harvard topper with work experience in the Big Apple. (It was almost unheard of for a lawyer to relocate from New York City, the temple of law practice, to a smaller city like Baltimore.) Four years later, she joined Shapiro & Olander. At both the places, Sheela Murthy helped to start their immigration law departments. It was funny that because she was an immigrant herself and a woman of color, and for no other apparent reason, she became the automatic choice for the job. But in doing so, she set the ball in motion for the conception of what would one day become one of the finest and most successful immigration law firms in the world—the Murthy Law Firm.

18

It began with one lawyer, Sheela Murthy, and one client, an Iranian doctor. It began on Saturday, 7 May 1994. The client had originally approached Shapiro & Olander requesting an appointment for Monday, 9 May, for a consultation over an immigration matter. He was informed that their lone immigration attorney, Ms Sheela Murthy, had resigned; Friday, 6 May was to be her last day at the firm. He was also informed that, come Monday, Shapiro & Olander would no longer be able to take immigration cases. It was suggested that the client get in touch directly with The Law Office of Sheela Murthy, where, he was assured, his issue would be dealt with most effectively.

As it turned out, Ms Murthy's office was the dining table in Sheela and Vasant's little townhouse in Owings Mills, a suburb of Baltimore. It was equipped with a fax machine, a telephone and an old computer. It all began on a Saturday, a day offices across America were shut for the weekend. But Sheela had come home from her final day at work at Shapiro & Olander the previous evening, and the thought of waiting a whole weekend to kick-start her dream seemed like a colossal waste of time to her. So, when the telephone rang, and a distraught voice with a thick, Middle-Eastern accent said, 'Ms Murthy, may I come and meet you on Monday?' Sheela cheerfully replied: 'Oh no, *I* will come and meet *you*. Today.'

* * *

From coal worker's pneumoconiosis, the disease had progressed to necrosis of the lungs. Carla's father was dying.

'You should have followed the course of treatment more carefully,' the pulmonologist in Philadelphia admonished her sternly, 'It would have given him more time.' Carla dropped her eyes and said nothing. She had no words to describe the legal battle she had fought—and lost—over many years with the mining company her father had served, to demand that they honor their decades-old promise of health benefits for him. Without those benefits, she had not been able to afford the medicines the pulmonologist had prescribed on their previous visit to him. She made the journey back to West Virginia in silence—her mind too preoccupied to be aware of the old man slumped beside her in the passenger seat. His labored breathing had become a part of the ambient sound of her life. She hardly noticed it anymore. Her mind, instead, was looking ahead into a future that would stretch on interminably once her father was gone and she was left alone...

But the story itself was larger than Carla and her father. The story stretched to include all those families and communities that had lived in the vicinity of the coal mines of Appalachia, where mining had been the main business for over a hundred years. It expanded to encompass the men who had descended into the earth to mine coal, in the hope of giving their families a better life—all the while inhaling lethal dust that would turn their lungs into landmines waiting to explode, even as the mining companies they served grew richer.

The men fell sick, sooner or later. It was only a matter of time. The intrinsic poverty of the region resulted in seriously retarded healthcare infrastructure and not enough doctors to cope with the volume and seriousness of the illnesses. The mining companies routinely reneged on their promises of pension and health benefits to their retired employees, who had left their youth and health behind them, deep in the bowels of the earth.

* * *

Vasant drove Sheela to meet Dr Bashir Abdul Karimi, her very first client, at his residence. He was an Iranian national, newly graduated from medical school. He had come to the United States on a J-1 non-immigrant visa four years ago. The man was clearly impressed to see Sheela at his doorstep, crack on time. A personal visit from an experienced lawyer! He believed that he was getting some sort of VIP treatment. He never suspected the real reason—Sheela had no intention of letting clients discover that her 'office' was really just a dining table! No doubt they would turn around and leave if they did.

Seated in the living room, her feet sinking into the soft, Persian carpet at her feet, Sheela looked expectantly at the young man sitting across from her. He had thick black hair, and his dense eyebrows loomed over dark eyes, contrasting strongly against his fair skin. 'A typically Persian face,' she thought, as she uncapped her fountain pen and prepared to take notes. As it turned out, she did not need her notepad or pen. It was a pretty straightforward case.

'I arrived in America on a scholarship from my government. They paid for my medical education in this country.'

'I see,' responded Sheela. 'And?'

'And as per my visa status, the US government requires me to return to Iran to do a two-year residency there before I can reapply for a fresh visa.'

'True. You're on a J-1 visa, right? You're an IMG, an International Medical Graduate, so yes, you are required to leave the country once your medical education is complete.' Something in her confident manner reassured Bashir that he was in good hands.

'The problem is that I do not want to go back to Iran. It is a restrictive country in so many ways, and it will be a difficult life to return to, Sheela. The customs, the traditions I grew up with so unquestioningly, now no longer make sense to me. It is a beautiful country, don't get me wrong. But I don't think I will ever be able to adjust to living there again. And once I return, I will never be allowed to come back. There is too much family there, too many expectations. It isn't just my parents. There are aunts, uncles, siblings, cousins, grand aunts and grand uncles … they will look for a bride and get me married, my family is keen to set up a practice for me … my life will be taken over completely!' He broke off helplessly, and shrugged in despair.

Sheela was silent for a long time. She was thinking of a solution. But she was also weighing the ethics of this case. Doctors in the US usually made a lot of money. Many who picked the medical profession and slogged their way through years and years of med school, residency and specialization did so because they knew what kind of fat paychecks awaited them at the end of the long road. Yet, how many became doctors to genuinely serve humankind? In a country like Iran, there were people who could do well with the kind of healthcare a highly trained medical professional like Dr Karimi could provide.

She thought of her father-in-law, Dr Shankar Nayak, back home in India. She thought of the years he had spent in small villages and towns trying to help the poor and to eradicate disease; of how he never spoke of his hardships, except when recounting them as a funny incident here, an amusing anecdote there. What would he say to this young man? What advice would he give?

'There is another thing,' said Bashir, cutting across Sheela's thoughts. 'My sister, who is married and settled in Ohio, has offered to sponsor my green card. She is the only one who understands the dilemma I am faced with, and she wants to help me out of it. But

I do not want to accept her help because it will put a tremendous financial strain on her. Her husband and she run a small grocery store in Beachwood, Ohio. They don't make a lot of money.'

Sheela nodded. She turned to look out of the window to where their car was parked. It was the car that she had bought with the money she had made working as student campus security at Harvard. She could afford a lot better now, but she was sentimental about the car. Vasant, perceptive and sensitive as always, had never tried to talk her into selling it. He understood that to her, this car had been her first step towards achieving her dream of independence in a country that had come to epitomize freedom in the eyes of the world. She could clearly see Vasant sitting in the driver's seat, reading a book. His profile was so like his father's.

Suddenly she knew what advice she should give to this doctor.

'Bashir,' she said, turning back to him and meeting his eyes directly. 'This is a rich country, much more than the one you have left behind. I know that there are practical considerations and personal choices behind you wanting to remain in America, and I don't question that. But a doctor's first duty is to bring health to the sick, preferably to those who badly need it.'

Bashir sat forward, listening to her keenly, a frown marking his heavy brow.

'The immigration laws of this country have very recently—as recently as this year, in fact—formulated and expanded a new one that permits an International Medical Graduate to remain in the country and practice medicine in America, immediately after completing an MD.'

Bashir's face lit up with hope, but he said nothing.

'It is called a J-1 Visa Waiver program,' went on Sheela. 'The condition is that he or she must be willing to serve in a Medically Underserved Area—an MUA—or a Health Professional Shortage Area (HPSA), for a minimum of three years.'

Bashir rose from his seat and went into the kitchen where the coffee had been put to brew. A minute later he returned with three steaming mugs on a tray. He laid one down in front of Sheela, and took the second mug outside to Vasant in the car. Sheela was surprised he had noticed that she had a traveling companion. When he returned to the room, he lifted his mug to his lips and took a sip. 'I get what you're saying, Sheela. I will do it. Where would I have to go?'

'Appalachia in West Virginia,' replied Sheela. 'There isn't a place in the United States more desperately in need of medical care, Bashir.'

19

A few months later, one Mr Jurgen Hans walked into the firm and introduced himself as the CEO of a major American multi-national company. 'But I head the European operations,' he added. His accent was an interesting mix of his native Germany and his adopted America. 'That means my work keeps me out of the country—*this* country—for long stretches of time. I am a permanent resident of the Unites States, Ms Murthy. I got my green card a little over fifteen years ago.'

He removed his handkerchief and passed it over his face. It was a cold day but he was clearly agitated and, in the course of the conversation, he was to repeat this action many more times. Sheela suspected it was more for comfort than to wipe the non-existent sweat from his brow. Putting down her pen, she requested her assistant to make him a cup of tea. He remained silent, staring moodily out of the window until she placed a mug before him. He accepted it quietly and resumed his narration.

'My company, as you know, is based out of Baltimore. Three days ago, I re-entered the US on a British Airways flight. I was flying in from London, after attending a series of conferences across Europe. When I got off the plane at the Baltimore-Washington International Airport, officers were waiting for me. They took me into secondary inspection and questioned me for hours. Four hours and twenty-eight minutes to be precise, Ms Murthy!'

Sheela was perturbed to learn this but at the same time couldn't contain a smile. The Germans were known for their precision, if not for anything else! At his next words, however, the smile faded.

'They wanted to know why I had chosen to remain outside the United States for large parts of the year even though I had obtained my green card fifteen years ago. They said that they had looked up my records and found that I only traveled to the US briefly several times a year. "It is to attend company meetings," I told them, and they said, "That is exactly the point we wish to understand, Mr Hans. Why do you enter this country, of which you are supposed to be a permanent resident, only to attend meetings?"'

Sheela frowned. They had a point. 'With a green card, you are expected to maintain your permanent resident status by remaining in the country for a minimum of 180 days, so it's true what they are saying. You have been away longer?'

'I don't know. I don't keep track. I am working, working, and for an *American* company at that. I go where the work takes me!' he cried indignantly.

'I understand, Mr Hans,' said Sheela placatingly, and she truly did. Here was a person who was so committed to his professional responsibilities that he had spared little thought for himself and his own well-being. A country he had given his life's blood to was now questioning his presence on its soil. He was not angry. He was hurt.

'I understand, but the authorities won't,' went on Sheela. 'You see, they follow the letter of the law, and they're just doing their job. They spare little thought for individual circumstances. Discretion plays no role in their line of work. Now a mistake has been made...'

'*Mistake?*' asked Jurgen.

'Yes, mistake,' insisted Sheela. She would take up this man's case and she would fight for him to the end. Sheela had come to love

America as her second home, and she knew instinctively that people like Jurgen Hans were good for it. It was people like him who made this country of immigrants stout of heart and strong of body. But she did need him to appreciate the consequences of his error, and the fact that even if she did succeed in getting him a second chance this time, there might not be a third one after that.

'It was a mistake to neglect the requirements of maintaining status,' she explained. 'You see, if a green card holder remains outside the country for 365 days or more, it is automatically assumed as abandonment of their permanent resident status. But if they are out of the country for between 180 and 364 days, the law *presumes* a person's intention to abandon his or her permanent resident status by choosing to reside elsewhere. So, those officers who took you in for questioning did have valid grounds for doing what they did.'

Jurgen looked thoughtful, even perplexed. But he was calmer now, more willing to listen. 'Why did they allow me into the country, in that case?' he asked.

'The law stipulates that all permanent residents have to be allowed into the country. Nobody can stop a green card holder from entering the United States. But I'm guessing that they issued you an NTA? A Notice to Appear?'

'Yes. I'm not sure what that is.' He pushed a piece of official-looking paper across the table to her. Sheela glanced at it.

'A court hearing. It is the first stage in the commencement of deportation proceedings. This one states that you have to be at the Baltimore Immigration Court on the 20th of this month at 9 a.m.'

'*Deportation?*' asked Jurgen, stunned.

Sheela nodded.

'And the hearing is ten days from now?'

'That's correct.'

Suddenly the dazed look left his eyes and was slowly but surely replaced by steely determination. He said in a voice that was stronger, more purposeful, 'Ten days it is, then. And not one day more! I will not wait any longer than that. I have made sure that I entered the US within six months of my leaving it, each and every time. I have fulfilled that requirement. And I've paid my taxes to this country without once defaulting. But now I have to return to Europe because there are important meetings to attend, a business to run. There are people looking to me for major decisions that will affect the fate of this company's overseas operations. If I have to wait longer than ten days, then it will throw things into a spin and I may as well quit now. I *will* quit and return to the country of my birth immediately!' he finished defiantly.

'No,' said Sheela. 'I will not let you do that.' Jurgen opened his mouth to protest but Sheela went on to say, 'If you are deported, you will be barred from re-entering this country for a minimum of five years. And if you leave before the hearing is concluded, it will be taken as self-deportation, and that will be the nail in the coffin. You must not give up so quickly. You must wait and be patient.'

'He is like a child,' Sheela thought, 'This tall, large-framed gentleman with his bearded face and rumpled, graying hair. He does not understand the subtler rules along whose lines the world runs, or its twists and turns and manipulations. He believes that if he is true to his work then everything around him will fall into place.' Her heart went out to him.

'Will you represent me in court, Ms Murthy?' Jurgen Hans asked in a subdued voice.

'I certainly will.'

* * *

Sheela Murthy had never been to a court. She had been to a moot court all right but never an actual functioning court of law. She had no idea about its protocols and procedures, except for what she had read about in books or heard about from colleagues. What she did know was that she had to win this case.

Over the next ten days, she pondered over what she would argue, preparing her brief and gathering relevant information that Jurgen willingly handed over to her. She had his letter of employment with his current company, the payments he had made in full on his villa in Baltimore, the tax returns that he had filed since the day he had first arrived in America, among others.

On the morning of the 20th, Sheela reached the Baltimore Immigration Court half an hour prior to the time of the hearing, briefcase in hand. Jurgen was waiting for her outside, and they walked into the courthouse together. At precisely 9 a.m., they entered the courtroom, Sheela holding the EOIR 28 confirming her representation of the respondent, Mr Jurgen Hans. Judge Markle was presiding over the case. He was a stickler for protocol and followed the letter of the law to the T. Sheela, however, was blissfully unaware of this.

Once the court was in session, she looked up from her desk and met the judge's eyes with her own frank ones. Without waiting to consider, she proceeded to summarize the case in her succinct way. The judge glanced at the Immigration and Naturalization Service attorney, who was representing the federal government. The lady was watching Sheela with a bemused expression, and Judge Markle turned his attention back to Sheela.

'It was improper for the US Customs to have issued this NTA to my client when he was out of the country purely in service to his *American* company!' Sheela was saying passionately. 'His requirement to live outside of the US was necessitated entirely by virtue of his being transferred as head of the European operations of an American company. He draws his salary in US Dollars, and has paid income taxes in this country diligently for the past fifteen years in order to confirm his intention to maintain his permanent residence status in the US. He has a home here, Your Honor, one that he bought by taking out a loan that he paid off over several years, just so that when he retired, he would have a place to live in his own country, the United States.

'I have spoken to his company's finance department. They have put together the company's turnover from their overseas operations under my client's leadership, to give you an idea of just how much income was generated for America through his efforts.'

Sheela stepped forward and handed a file to the judge. She couldn't understand why he was staring at her so oddly, and frankly she did not care. She didn't care about anything except telling the truth about Jurgen Hans and winning him the right to retain his green card.

'In there ...' she indicated the file, 'are Jurgen Hans' income tax returns, the bank loans on his house, the title deed of the property, everything. Everything in there is proof of his intention to maintain his permanent residence status in the US.'

The judge opened the file and skimmed through the documents inside. He lingered over the one from Jurgen's company regarding turnovers. The figures in there made his eyebrows go up.

'My client is leaving the country tomorrow. He *must*, or else millions of dollars more will be lost. As it is, these past ten days of waiting for this hearing has cost the company heavily in terms of business, reputation and money. In the process, Mr Hans will lose his job and his livelihood. So I respectfully request the court to terminate these proceedings, reinstate his permanent resident status and return the I-551 to him, so that he can travel on schedule tomorrow, Your Honor.'

There was a silence of a few seconds that seemed to last a few years. Had she done right, Sheela wondered. Having delivered her argument, she now had time to ponder over the accuracy of her presentation. After all, she had no previous experience to go by!

Judge Markle turned to the INS attorney, Ms Sarah Smith. 'Counselor, do you have anything to say about this?'

The attorney looked stumped. 'Er ... your honor, this is just the Master Calendar hearing, and I am not fully apprised of the details of the case. I am not prepared to argue on the substantive merits of the case at the moment. If I can be given a little more time...'

Judge Markle gave her long hard look and replied, 'Counselor, you've got to do what you've got to do and I've got to do what I've got to do. It's a waste of the court's time and the taxpayer's resources that a case like this had to be brought to court. If I give you more time and another hearing, I will be compounding those errors. You may convey to the US Customs officers that, in my opinion, they need better training.'

Ms Smith blinked, taken aback by this direct reprimand.

'Based on Ms Murthy's arguments,' went on the judge, 'I'm dismissing all charges against the respondent. Mr Hans, your permanent resident status is hereby reinstated. The Service will return your I-551to you immediately.' As he stood up and turned away, Sheela thought she heard him add with a shake of his head, 'I'm sorry you even had to go through this.'

The second Judge Markel left the courtroom, Jurgen Hans turned to Sheela and threw his arms around her in sheer delight and gratitude. 'Thank you!' he cried. 'Thank you for not letting me do anything stupid!' and Sheela laughed.

As they left the courtroom, a senior lawyer named Anne Speigleman who had been present at the hearing, walked up to Sheela and said sternly, 'Young lady, do you know what just happened in there?'

Sheela smiled vaguely.

'Hmm. I see you have no idea what I'm talking about. Good for you. That's probably why you won this case.'

'What do you mean?' asked Sheela.

'Have you ever heard of a Master Calendar hearing?' asked Ms Speigleman.

'No.'

'This your first time in court?'

Sheela grinned sheepishly. 'Was it obvious?'

'Came through loud and clear!' replied the senior attorney briskly. 'The first hearing is always a Master Calendar hearing. You just establish yourself as the attorney on the case, and the court sets a date for the next hearing. No arguments or verdicts take place in a Master Calendar hearing. Judge Markle knows that. Everybody does.'

Sheela's jaw dropped open in horror. A glimmer of sardonic humor sparkled in Anne's grey-ringed eyes. Clearly, she enjoyed being the one to shock the young lawyer, even while it was obvious that she liked her.

'I have been practicing law in these parts for twenty-seven years now. I have never known Judge Markle to sidestep protocol like he did today.' Suddenly Anne Speigleman smiled. 'You are either very dumb or you're very bright, Miss Murthy. I shall keep my eye on you until I find out which!'

20

Vasant went on to teach the master's program in digital arts that he had designed and created, to numerous students in the years to come, losing himself completely in his work. Sheela noticed that many of his students felt that they had a deep and meaningful connection with him. It did not surprise her. She thought of her husband as a superlative human being who was compassionate, sensible and steady. So it was only natural that others too would find him so. As students brought their assignments to Vasant for a critique, his power of discernment necessarily led him to put his finger on the deeper sub-texts of the work. So, very often, a simple submission would end in a long, one-on-one personal conversation in which his students opened up their hearts to him and shared aspects of their personal life, their difficulties and the pain, which he had more often than not already discovered from mere observation.

Over time, Vasant ceased to merely be a professor. He became a mentor, a teacher and a guide. A friend too. Self-effacing and utterly oblivious to his own merits, he failed to notice the effect he had on those around him, maintaining the same kindly humility with all. Vasant Nayak was probably one of the most beloved teachers on the MICA campus. And then, one day, he quit.

The reasons were multifold. The first was that he felt himself getting inexorably pulled into the daily workings of the outside world, his inner silence being taken over by hectic external activity and incessant interaction. He knew that it would affect his ability to *be* in this world—to create and to maintain the purity of his art, as well as the artist within. The second reason was that he was excited about the prospect of putting Sheela on the World Wide Web in its infancy. Third, he felt that Sheela needed him. He watched her put in fourteen-, sometimes eighteen-hour workdays, day after day, that first year. She was struggling to make her law firm into a presence to contend with in the field of immigration law. He knew that there were aspects of its running that he could take upon himself most effectively, freeing her to simply concentrate on the actual task of fighting cases and helping her clients. That the firm was making money was certain. But Vasant felt instinctively that it had not come anywhere close to its full potential yet. There was a small staff of paralegals that worked along with Sheela. Like her, they were overworked, stressed beyond endurance, and burning their candles at both ends. Not surprisingly, the attrition rate was high. Probably the only thing that was keeping Sheela herself from throwing in the towel was the fact that this was *her* law firm, her baby. Probably the only baby she would ever have.

There was no doubt in Vasant's mind now that Sheela and he should never have children. She was overwhelmingly busy, utterly committed to her life as a lawyer and rapidly gaining recognition in her field. At this time, a baby would change everything. And if he were to take over the responsibility of raising the child and free her to work, his own life would take a different path altogether, one he was not certain he wanted to tread.

In 1994, the Internet was a relatively new technology. Vasant had taught his students at MICA to build websites to showcase their art. His own work was now online and visible to anybody who was sitting in any corner of the world. With web technology being at a nascent stage, he used to painstakingly hand-code every bit of information before uploading it. But the effort was worth it; Vasant recognized the World Wide Web as a tool, a medium of tremendous potential. When he finally quit MICA—to the great dismay of his students and colleagues—he joined the Law Office of Sheela Murthy as a consultant and as their Internet expert.

'Put up information on the website that I am going to build for you, Sheelu,' he said one day.

'A website? What for?' asked Sheela, looking up distractedly from one of her briefs as they both sat working at their dining table one night after dinner. The dining table had long ceased to be Sheela's office but had remained her favorite place to work even after she had shifted operations to a more sophisticated workspace!

'So that the whole world will get to know of your existence. Not just the people at Owings Mills or Baltimore or in a few cities in America, but also people in India, in Uzbekistan, and in the farthest corners of the world. How will you ever reach out to them, otherwise? How will they find you when they need your help?'

Sheela put down her pen and listened in silence, for what he was saying made sense. 'What information do you want me to put up?'

'Everything there is to know about immigration law. Rules, policies, daily updates in federal regulations that will affect the life of an immigrant or a potential immigrant. Put it out there in simple language, Sheelu. The person reading it should not have to have a law degree to understand what you are telling them on your website.'

Sheela was aghast! Upload information on the Internet for free that other lawyers and firms charged thousands of dollars to impart to their clients!

'I know what you're thinking,' said Vasant. Her face was expressive, and after nearly a decade of marriage, he could read it like a book. 'But just consider this, Sheelu. Knowledge is free. It *should* be. Nobody should have to pay money to find out something that is their right to know. Life has been good to us. Let's pass on the goodness to those who need it. People will get on your website, they will find out what they need to know, they will gain clarity and some semblance of peace. What you do as a lawyer is something that no amount of information can replace. Giving people information will never get in the way of that. It will only empower people to fulfill their dreams a little more easily.'

Nobody should have to pay money to find out something that is their right to know. Sheela felt something powerful grip her heart.

'I'll work with you as soon as I'm done with this case,' she said suddenly, coming to a decision as directly and effortlessly as a child, which was her way. 'We'll put together all the information on immigration and the latest changes in federal policies on immigration—whatever we can think of that will be useful on a website like this.'

It is not as if Sheela didn't have misgivings. But she trusted Vasant implicitly, trusted his good sense and generosity. If he thought it was a good idea, then she had no doubt that someday very soon she would come to share his point of view as well. When Sheela didn't see eye to eye with Vasant, she never doubted his stand. She usually questioned her own. There was no other person in the world she did this with, not even Daddy whom she loved beyond all others and yet knew to be flawed in so many ways (lovable and forgivable though she found those flaws!)

And so, not long after that fateful conversation at the dining table, MurthyDotCom was born.

Vasant was right. It was an instant hit and went on to become the largest immigration law website in the world, drawing upward of three million views each month. This was more than what the next ten most-frequented legal websites put together drew! The information on MurthyDotCom was so up-to-date, so accurate and user-friendly that, before long, the US Department of Naturalization and Immigration, which has since been renamed the United States Citizenship and Immigration Services (USCIS), began to urge its employees to get onto Sheela Murthy's website to learn more about immigration, particularly about immigration from an immigrant's perspective.

Sheela's business grew by leaps and bounds. She was no longer a one-person team. With steady growth in business, she was able to shift the Law Office of Sheela Murthy to a modern office building in Owings Mills within the very first year of the firm's inception. It was situated close to the compact townhouse she shared with Vasant. For a monthly rent of $300, Sheela now had an office of her own and access to a conference room. The rent came with built-in services of a receptionist and a photocopier machine, both of which she shared with a fellow tenant. Vasant heaved a sigh of relief to see her go. He had just about had enough of having his home invaded by Sheela's law practice!

With the rapidly increasing demand on her time, Sheela and her team of four paralegals were now working round the clock. While the team helped with the research, the preparation and filing of paperwork, Sheela was the sole lawyer operating behind it all. Therefore, the responsibility of every client who walked in through the doors of her firm came to rest squarely on her shoulders. Her sense of commitment to each of them, her predisposition to perfection in everything she undertook, did not permit her to take short cuts. Every client had to be given personal time and attention that resulted in a positive solution. Each one had to leave her office satisfied and with a sense of well-being.

To achieve those ends, Sheela rose early each morning, completed her household chores, and went in to work by 8 a.m. From the moment she set foot in office, there were back-to-back appointments. Restroom breaks were often delayed until they could be postponed no further! Lunch was a hurriedly swallowed meal, whatever went down quickest, regardless of whether it was healthy or not. It was eaten with one eye on the clock because the next appointment was always just minutes away. What would Indu have said to this? Her mother, who had insisted that every meal be balanced and nutritious, eaten slowly, chewed well and in complete silence, so that the mind would engage with the food during the process. What would she have said about Sheela's makeshift lunches and bolted-down dinners? What would Colonel Murthy have said if he had found out that his Sheela no longer had time to sleep, to laugh or to meet her friends? Sheela was preserved from thinking of the answers to these questions because she simply didn't have the time to do that. Had she weighed herself, the scales would have told her that she had gained several pounds. But at 7 a.m. each day, it never struck her to climb onto the scales in the bathroom, so she never knew. When she returned home sixteen hours later, it was just enough time for a reheated dinner before she fell into bed, often well past midnight. On the weekends, she took care of all the other work of the firm—accounting, marketing, client calls and case work. But all these sacrifices were necessary, Sheela convinced herself. Fifty per cent of all businesses that were started in America in those days, folded within the first five years of being established. She'd be damned if the Law Office of Sheela Murthy made it into that list!

Matters went on in this way until one day, in 1998, four years after the firm's inception, three out of Sheela's four paralegals handed in their notices, all within the span of a single week. Sheela, who had become more and more engrossed in her work and consequently less and less aware of the reality around her, was horrified! On one of the nights, she came as close to despondency as she had been on that distant day, after her long illness and confinement in Delhi. But she had promised never to let herself be overcome by such feelings again, and although she had been but a child when she made that promise, she had never once broken it. She was not about to do so now.

'What is it? What's the matter?' asked Vasant, wandering up with his book in hand. She told him. To her surprise, he smiled.

'Why is this funny?' she demanded indignantly.

'Do you remember why you quit White & Case?' asked Vasant.

'Because my bosses were monsters who slogged me out and I didn't have a moment's rest or—'

Vasant said nothing, merely watched her silently until realization dawned.

'You mean … Oh! But … it isn't only my paralegals; *I* work just as hard. Harder, even!' she cried.

'So did your bosses at your first job, didn't they?' probed Vasant.

'M … maybe, I guess. I mean they did, you're right…' she stammered, and then, after a very long pause, she slowly concluded, 'You're right. I've become just like them.'

'Your team wants to *live*, Sheelu. To breathe and sleep and spend time at home with their families. When did you last speak with your father, or visit him?'

Sheela stared at Vasant blankly. Four years. Four years it had been since she had last seen Daddy. And every time she called him (which was rarely enough, god knew) he always asked, 'When are you coming home, Sheela?' Tears started in her eyes and she blinked them back.

'My team quit because I've become my ex-bosses. I've become the monster that is driving my team the way they drove me,' she mumbled.

Vasant only smiled, letting her draw her own conclusions. But he knew Sheela well. If anybody had the ability to recognize their error and rectify it in an instant, it was this wife of his. He knew that after today, business at the Law Office of Sheela Murthy would never be conducted in the same manner again.

* * *

Lesley Amano joined the Law Office of Sheela Murthy in August 1998. By this time, the firm was renting two floors in the office building to accommodate its team of one attorney and eighteen paralegals. Lesley was the second attorney to come on board. She was hardworking, bright and knowledgeable, and she cared. She really cared. On her very first day at work, at 7 p.m., she looked up from a brief about a case that she was going to be taking over from Sheela, and remarked, 'Until yesterday, you were doing all the work that you are doing right now, and my portion of it too? All by yourself! Wow. It's a wonder you didn't have a breakdown!'

'I was too busy to have one!' laughed Sheela. But despite the humor, she once again found herself fighting back tears. As she watched Lesley lower her head over the brief again, she took a deep breath and let it out slowly. For the first time, she felt that she was no longer fighting alone. For the first time, there was someone there who had her back.

For the first time in nearly five years, she was taking time off from work to go home to Daddy.

21

The parents were Indian. The child, having been born in the United States, was an American citizen. The mother, Swati, made an appointment to speak with Sheela over the phone for a consultation. When the call was put through by Reggie, Sheela's executive assistant at that time, the women was weeping so desperately that she was incoherent, and Sheela had to wait a while for the torrent of emotion to pass.

'He hates us both. He won't even look at Nina. I don't believe he has ever picked her up, not once in these four years since she was born. One day, when she was just a few months old, I had put Nina down for her nap. Her father was watching TV in the next room, and so I thought it would be all right to step out to the 7-Eleven up the road to pick up a few essentials. When I got back, Nina was screaming, and Nitin was sitting there watching TV as if nothing had happened. He had turned up the volume to drown out the sound of her crying. That is when I first knew that something was seriously wrong.'

Sheela jotted down the points of the case on her note pad as she listened to Swati speak. Father—cold, indifferent. Parents—Indian citizens. Child—American.

'What is your relationship with Nitin like?' asked Sheela, sensing instinctively that Swati had reached a point in this marriage where to refer to Nitin as her husband no longer made sense.

'He hates me, I think. He hasn't touched me since I conceived Nina, except when being violent, and he barely speaks with me. He comes home, eats dinner in front of the TV and then goes to bed. In the morning, he leaves for work again. He is having an affair with some woman at his office, which I found out through one of his colleagues. Anyway, I'm past the point of caring. It's a relief, actually. But let me tell you the really weird thing in all this, Ms Murthy. If I am not home when he gets in—if I happen to leave Nina at day care to go for a yoga class or a game of squash, whatever, he goes nuts! He turns violent, breaks things around the house and—'

'Has he hit you?'

'Many times. And he starts accusing me of having an affair.'

'Do you want to stay in this marriage?' asked Sheela. She had learnt, over the years of working in this field, never to take anything for granted. What seemed so obvious to a third person about a discordant relationship was often completely invisible to the parties involved. For all she knew, Swati might be this upset because she was looking for a way to resolve things with Nitin.

'No!' came the answer, promptly and clearly. 'I'm looking for a way to take my child and go back home to India.'

'What is stopping you?'

'He is, that bastard!' exclaimed Swati. 'I asked him for a divorce and he flatly refused. He said he would never give me the permission to take Nina out of this country. I just don't understand it, Ms Murthy. When he hates us so much, I just don't understand why he wants us around!'

'He clearly has some issues to deal with. Is he seeing a therapist? If he is, then perhaps the therapist may be able to talk to him,' suggested Sheela.

'He will physically assault me if I suggest that he is mentally unstable. The one time I did, he became violent and broke things in the house.' Suddenly, Swati burst out, 'Please help me, Ms Murthy! I have consulted other lawyers and they all tell me that there is nothing that they can do to help. They say that my hands are tied by the law and it does not permit me, the mother, to take my own child out of this country without the consent of her father because she is a US citizen! I just want to go home. I want to go home to my parents. I haven't seen them in four years, not since Nina was born, because Nitin has flatly refused to let her go, and I will never leave without Nina. I know that if I do I will never see her again!'

What followed was another paroxysm of weeping, and Sheela took a deep breath. Her innate intolerance of cruelty or injustice of any kind made her bile rise to her throat whenever she heard a story like this. But she knew now that letting her own emotions get in the way would hamper her ability to manage the distraught Swati and think clearly at the same time.

'Swati,' said Sheela firmly. 'Try to calm down and listen carefully to what I have to say.'

There was silence on the other end, except for the continued sobbing that had now grown less intense. Sheela waited for the sound to subside further before asking again, 'You're listening, Swati?'

'Yes,' Swati managed to hiccup.

'Those other lawyers were right. The law is unbending on the point of letting a minor citizen of this country leave US soil without the consent of both the parents. There is nothing to be done about it. So, we will have to think of a different track now. Do your parents know anybody in India who is powerful or influential enough to take your case to the Indian government?

'How will that help?' asked Swati.

'I'm wondering if it is possible for us to seek help from the External Affairs Ministry of India to issue Nina an Indian passport,' explained Sheela. 'That is known to have happened before. As an Indian national stranded outside the country, they are responsible for your well-being, no matter where in the world you may be.'

There was a short silence on the other end, and then Swati said, 'My parents know some people. They are good family friends, in fact,' and she mentioned a name that Sheela immediately recognized would carry weight with the government back home.

'Speak to your friends. Tell them to get Nina an Indian passport. The Ministry of External Affairs will co-operate once they are apprised of the details of the case. Nina may be an American citizen, but she is of Indian origin and her mother is Indian, so they will never leave her stranded in another country with a mentally unstable father.'

'If we approach the Ministry without these friends' involvement?'

'They will still intervene and help. Only, it may take a little longer.'

'I will call my mother, Ms Murthy,' said Swati, and rang off.

A day went by, then three days. But when Swati called back, she sounded more cheerful.

'They immediately offered help, Ms Murthy! When my mother told them about the situation, they were very kind and concerned. They have begun the process of establishing contact with Delhi!'

Sheela smiled in relief. 'That is terrific news, Swati! Now listen, there's another thing you will have to do. You will need to request that when the passport is issued, it should be mailed to some other address, not your home one. Definitely not to your home where Nitin might find it and take it away. You understand?'

'Yes, of course, I will ask my friend if I can give her address as the mailing address.'

'Only if this friend is someone you trust completely. It is a good idea not to tell anybody about this until it happens. Because, if word reaches Nitin, he can get a restraining order or pull some other stunt, which will leave you stranded. Once the passport is in your hand, you are free to leave America and take Nina with you back to India where you will both be safe. And Swati?'

'Yes, Ms Murthy?'

'Don't say goodbye to anybody here. Just leave. You can get in touch with people once you are back in India and explain the situation then. But no explanations or goodbyes until you are out of this country. Okay?'

Swati left the United States of America in September 1999, with her four-year-old daughter Nina. They returned to Chandigarh, where Swati's parents took them in and helped Swati get back on her feet. Once his wife and daughter had left him, Nitin lost interest in them completely. When served with divorce papers two months later, he signed without a murmur, handing over full custody of Nina to Swati on the condition that she would ask for no alimony or child maintenance from him. Swati, who wanted nothing more than to sever all ties with him, readily agreed. Swati got a job in Bangalore and went on to make a name for herself in the field of advertising. She remains friends with Sheela to this day. Swati and Nina never set foot in America again.

22

The marriage was arranged by the bridegroom's mother and the bride's uncle. But for Sharat Joshi, it was love at first sight. He had barely got time off from work to attend his own wedding, having joined a medical conglomerate in Washington D.C., just a few months prior. His mother, back in Mumbai, had informed him that they had found a suitable bride for him.

In the Indian context, arranged marriages were commonplace. The elders in the family selected a potential partner for their offspring, keeping cultural background, financial status and education in mind before introducing the couple in a formal setting for a possible marriage.

Sharat was warm, generous and easy-going by nature. People in his company—his boss and his co-workers—liked him immensely, and the two housemates who he shared the apartment with treated him like family. Sharat looked forward to getting married and having someone of his own to love and share his life with. And especially now that he had this job that made it possible for him to live away from his parents' home in Mumbai. It was not that he didn't care for them. On the contrary, Sharat was an affectionate son. But he had honestly accepted the reality that his mother was rather overbearing, and while he and his father had learnt to make peace with her interference in the minute workings of their lives, Sharat did not feel that it was right to expect the woman he married to have to do the same.

In India, the joint family system was still very prevalent. In all likelihood, had he not moved to the US, he would have been expected to get a job in Mumbai and continue to stay at home with his parents even after getting married.

'She is very pretty!' Mrs Joshi had gushed into the phone to her son in faraway America. 'She is tall, fair, slim…'

The Indian obsession with color matched that of any country around the world, where lighter skin carried a premium when it came to almost anything. In India, however, fair skin carried no greater value anywhere else than in the marriage market! As Mrs Joshi had hurried into the kitchen to put away the dishes in which she had served delicacies to the bride's family, her husband came on the line and said in a low voice to his son, 'Sharat, don't you want to get to know the girl first before you decide?'

'*Aai* seems to have already given an answer to the girl's family, *Baba*,' replied Sharat uncertainly. The father heaved a sigh. It was true; his wife *had* given her consent to the bride's family and had even gone as far as to fix the date of the wedding. All without consulting him or their son. 'Of course, it would never strike her to do something like ask us our opinion!' thought Mr Joshi, who had his private reservations about the way this whole affair had turned out. There didn't seem to be anything wrong with the girl. She was, as his wife described, very pretty. But it took more than good looks to make a happy marriage, and his son was such a good, gentle soul…

'*Baba*, don't worry about *Aai*,' said Sharat. 'If I am to get married, why not this girl, since I haven't found anybody suitable for myself in all these years? At least we know the family backgrounds match, and that her folks are decent.'

'Sharat…' began his father helplessly.

'America only knows love marriages, *Baba*. The concept of arranged marriages doesn't exist here. And yet, this country is filled with divorcees,' reasoned Sharat, who knew that his father suffered from a heart condition, and did not want him stressing about this matter any further. Sharat knew his mother well enough to know that once she had made up her mind, there was no stopping her. The rest of the family would simply have to fall in with her plans. Anything else would lead to quarrels and unpleasantness, and Sharat did not want to expose his father to any of that.

'I'll make it work, *Baba*,' he said.

'She has fixed up the wedding at two weeks from now!' exclaimed the old gentleman.

There was a long pause. Then slowly, Sharat repeated, 'I'll make it work.'

* * *

'Sheela, your 3.30 p.m. appointment is here. Shall I send him in?'

'Yes, thank you, Reggie,' replied Sheela, putting away a case file that she had been poring over, in preparation to meet her next client. She glanced at her almanac. It said, Sharat Joshi.

The door opened and a good-looking man in his late twenties walked in. He looked harassed and worn. Sheela rose from her chair and extended her hand. Under her kind, cheerful smile, Sharat immediately relaxed. He had come here with a lot of hope. After running from pillar to post these past three years, from one lawyer to the next, and paying thousands of dollars in consultation fees, somebody had finally suggested that he must approach Sheela Murthy, the reputed immigration lawyer from Owings Mills.

'She's said to be the goddess of immigration law!' the well-wisher had informed him, which had, for some reason, made Sharat even more nervous. But the person standing before him did not seem like an unapproachable goddess. She seemed like a very real human being made of flesh and blood, whose eyes sparkled with a mixture of laughter and compassion. He liked her immediately. And for the first time in three years, Sharat felt the sickening sensation of despair loosen its grip around his heart.

'She is threatening to divorce me, Ms Murthy. And I don't blame her! We have met a handful of times in the three years that we've been married, that's all. Her family has been urging her to break up with me and return home to them. "What is the point of living with in-laws when the husband is not around?" they say. And they are right in their own way, Ms Murthy...'

There was a short silence, in which Sheela sensed that he was struggling to say something more.

'You see,' he added slowly, 'my mother is not the easiest person in the world to get along with. Priya thought she would be living in America after marriage. I don't think she planned on living with in-laws...' he trailed off sadly.

'Did she say that she wanted to divorce you because of your mother?' asked Sheela, although she knew the question was not really relevant. It is just that she wanted to get a larger sense of the situation before she decided whether to take this case.

Sharat hesitated. 'Er ... I don't know exactly. I guess it's a combination of things. The whole community is speaking ill of me and my family for cheating a girl in this manner.'

'No point going down this track,' thought Sheela. 'Better get to the actual case itself.'

'Tell me what the problem is, Sharat. Start from the beginning, please.'

'Priya and I got married three years ago—two years and eight months to be precise, ma'am. My mother met and approved the alliance; I was in the US working for a company in North Carolina. I still am, actually.'

'You live in North Carolina?' asked Sheela.

'Yes, ma'am.'

'You've come all the way from there for a twenty-minute consultation?' she asked, taken aback.

'Yes.'

'You could have made an appointment over the phone, Sharat—'

'I wanted to meet you in person, Ms Murthy. I was told that if anyone could help me it was you. I wanted to come in person,' he assured her. He wasn't the first to say this. Plenty of clients came in to personally meet Sheela from the neighboring states. Some had even flown in all the way from the west coast. But it always pained her that they went through the trouble and the expense to do so, when she would have gladly done her best to help them regardless.

Sharat continued with his story. 'I flew back to India for the wedding that happened just two weeks after the families first met. But both sides had been in a hurry for the wedding and so I went ahead with it.'

Sheela opened her mouth to say something before she suddenly recalled that she too had known that she wanted to marry Vasant, the first time she had set eyes on him. How different was Sharat's situation from hers, really? She closed her mouth and waited for him to continue.

'After the wedding, I returned alone to the US, and three months later we applied for the H-4 dependent visa for Priya. The consulate in Mumbai denied it. We went through a travel agent, we tried repeatedly. Each time, they rejected our application. They questioned the validity of the marriage because of that initial three-month delay in filing for the dependent visa.'

'Why did you wait that long though?' asked Sheela.

'I had been given no time to plan before the wedding, Ms Murthy. It happened so suddenly that when I returned to the US after the ceremony, it was to the same tiny apartment I had been sharing with two friends. I thought that if I stayed on a little while longer, I would be able to scrimp and save for a nicer house, one that Priya would be proud to come home to when she landed in America. Besides, it would have been unfair of me to leave my housemates in the lurch. We were all fairly new in America. For all three of us, it was our first job. If I had left abruptly, they would have had a problem coughing up my share of the rent. And who knew how long it would have taken them to find another housemate?'

Sheela watched the young man closely as he spoke. He was so earnest and conscientious. This man, sitting before her, was a good person.

Unaware of the lawyer's thoughts, Sharat continued, 'My wife has been staying with my parents because my mother is traditional in her ways and expects it. It has been close to three years but we've had no success in bringing her across to America. The lawyers here have nothing to say, no solution to give. Priya and her parents are furious. I was on the verge of quitting my job and moving back to India but that upset Priya even further, Ms Murthy. She said that the whole community is talking about me and how I conned her into marriage before abandoning her. Apparently, they are saying that I am involved with another woman in America and so am avoiding bringing my wife to join me.'

Sheela stopped listening to him at this point. Her mind was running rapidly over the various options. In the meantime, Sharat was saying, 'Coming to you was my last hope. After this, if something doesn't work out, no matter what Priya or anyone else says, I will move back—'

'Did you find a house?' cut in Sheela abruptly.

'Yes. Within three months of returning to the US after my wedding, I found one.'

'And how soon did you apply for the H-4 for Priya?'

'Immediately after that,' he replied.

'Hmm. How immediately?'

'Er ... immediately, ma'am.'

'Good. Do you still have the rental agreement that you and your friends had signed at your old apartment?'

'I guess I must be having it in my file at home.'

'Are you certain?'

'I am, Ms Murthy,' he reaffirmed more confidently.

'And the agreement on the house that you took on rent after that?'

'Not rent, bought.'

'Loan?'

'Yes. And I have the bank loan papers. And the EMIs that go directly from my bank account towards paying off the loan.'

Sheela smiled. He was starting to get her drift, she could see. 'What about records of the first time you filed for the H-4?'

'I'm pretty sure Priya has it with her.'

'E-mail exchanges? Any messages that went back and forth between you two that would prove that there was affection and this was not just a marriage of convenience?'

Sharat colored and looked down at his hands in his lap. 'Yes. Many. From my end, at least. Many angry ones from hers.' He smiled faintly.

'Those will work too. Anything that you don't mind sharing will come in handy. Even anger shows that she was invested in this relationship, if it is the right sort of anger.'

'I don't mind sharing them, Ms Murthy,' replied Sharat, looking up and meeting her eyes frankly.

Sheela nodded, satisfied. 'I know you've been through hell, Sharat. I'm really sorry for what you've had to go through. But you've fought this battle for three years on your own. Now I'm asking you to give me three months to fight for you. Will you do that?'

Slowly Sharat smiled, a sense of hope entering his eyes. 'I will.'

* * *

One week after Sharat Joshi first stepped into Sheela Murthy's office, the American Consulate in Mumbai, India, received a fresh application for an H-4 dependent visa for Mrs Priya Joshi. Along with it were all the documents that proved that Sharat Joshi, her husband, had systematically worked towards bringing his wife to the United States, from the day he returned to the country after his wedding. There were the rental papers that proved that he had continued to live in a small, shared apartment in order to save money to buy a better place, the bank loan he took out in order to make a down payment on the new house, and the documents that proved that the H-4 for his wife had been first filed the very day after the down payment on the house had been made. There were also printouts of some interesting exchanges of emails between the couple that made the Consular Officer grin and thank god he had never married!

A month later, Priya Joshi received her passport from the American Consulate in Mumbai, with the H-4 visa stamped on it. Two weeks after that, she found herself on American soil, and ensconced in a beautiful little home of her own. Priya was happy at last. Both husband and wife wrote to Sheela, thanking her for reuniting them, signing their names at the bottom of the letter that Sharat insisted they write by hand because it was so much more personal than e-mail.

Sheela smiled when the letter reached her, because Sharat's face kept coming up in her mind as she read those words.

23

Aron Finklestein was in his final year of law school when his professor, an immigration judge, walked into class looking excited.

'There is this website I came across that I want you guys to take a look at,' he said. 'There's a lot to learn about immigration law from there. Plenty of useful, unbiased information, just the facts, no opinions.' He gave them the URL, and Aron, back in his dorm that evening, got onto the website. It was, indeed, hugely informative. He had a paper to hand in for one of his classes by the end of that week, which was just two days away. He should have begun work on it but instead found himself glued to the computer screen, pouring over the MurthyDotCom website, unable to tear himself away.

So began Aron Finkelstein's very long association with the Law Office of Sheela Murthy. If anybody had told him that day that he would someday be the third lawyer to join that firm, would go on to become Managing Attorney and would remain there for twenty years, Aron wouldn't have believed them. Dreams such as those were, after all, too good to come true.

Or, then again, maybe not.

Aron joined the Law Office of Sheela Murthy in October 1999. It was the most grueling interview any attorney was ever subjected to—in his opinion, at least! The fact is that his one year at a litigating law firm in downtown Baltimore right after he graduated law school had thrown him in the path of immigration law. It had grabbed his interest. So, in June of 1999, when he found out that Sheela Murthy, the up-and-coming immigration lawyer from Owings Mills, was hiring, he applied at once.

First, there was a written exam, which tested the mettle of the applicant to the fullest. Aron returned home that evening dejected.

'I'm sure I flunked the test,' he said to Elisheva.

'Oh, don't be so pessimistic,' she scolded her husband with a laugh. 'Wait for them to reject you before you reject yourself!'

As it turned out, he made it to the next round. At the interview, Aron found himself sitting across the table from Sheela and the other lawyer who worked at the firm. 'At least I know a thing or two about immigration law,' he consoled himself, seconds before Sheela flashed her warm smile and began to fire questions at him.

It turned out that he didn't know that much, after all. And this time he dared not go home and tell Elisheva about what a disaster this interview had turned out to be. She would find out soon enough when he wouldn't get the job.

But, he got the job.

'Why?' he asked Sheela incredulously, some weeks after he joined the firm. '*Why*? I'm sure I flunked that written test.'

'That was not a pass or fail test. I give that test to know the applicant's strengths as a lawyer. Anybody can gain knowledge if they've been in the field long enough. But nobody can learn instinct, at least not from a book. That is just something you're born with. You either have it or you don't. You've got that instinct, Aron. That test showed me that you are very good at spotting issues, which is why I want you on my team. Now, why aren't you eating the pizza?'

It was pizza day at the firm and the team was sitting around enjoying lunch, Sheela as much as anybody!

'Er ... kosher ... I keep kosher,' confessed Aron hesitantly. That was the first time Sheela had heard the term, and she asked him what it meant.

'It's a dietary restriction imposed by the Jewish faith. We follow it quite strictly at home, so...'

Sheela nodded and turned away. Aron was afraid that he had offended or disappointed her. But as Sheela rose to put away her plate, she only said, 'I plan to train you myself, Aron. You will spend an hour with me in the evenings over the next few months, and we will go over cases together. Okay?'

'Y ... yes. Sure. Thanks, Sheela.'

'I'll see you at 6.30 p.m. in my office,' she called over her shoulder as she walked away.

The following week, on pizza day, there was regular pizza for the whole team and the kosher variety for Aron. He knew, then, that there would be a lot for him to learn from Sheela Murthy. Not just about immigration law but about friendship, kindness and team spirit.

* * *

Sheela and Aron walked into the police precinct at 11.50 a.m. and asked to speak with the deputy. The uniformed cop who showed up ten minutes later, sipping coffee from an oversized mug, had a name badge on his chest that read—Jerry Marlowe.

Both attorneys rose to their feet and shook hands with him politely. When they introduced themselves, Marlowe's eyebrows shot up and he asked them if they'd like some coffee. Clearly, Sheela and her firm's reputation preceded her. The attorneys accepted the offer of coffee, and then followed Officer Marlowe into an interrogation room, where they would have some privacy in that noisy, bustling precinct to explain what it was they had come there for.

'We have a client called Mrs Kapoor. Mrs Arti Kapoor,' said Sheela, coming straight to the point. The cop was clearly busy and she didn't want to take up much of his time. 'Does that name sound familiar?'

'Vaguely.' He nodded slowly, trying to put his finger on who exactly she was referring to.

'Lives in…' and Aron supplied the lady's address.

'Yup, that's our jurisdiction all right,' said Marlowe.

'Indian woman. Domestic violence situation—'

'Got it!' said Marlowe. 'Came in early last month. Or rather, we brought her in, in response to a 911 call from a neighbor. She was beat up pretty bad.'

'Did you file a case?' questioned Sheela.

'No, ma'am.'

'Why not, officer?'

'Wasn't going to be no use filing one. That lady wasn't ever going to testify 'gainst her husband now, was she? If she had, we'da had him behind bars in a jiffy.'

'I see. It's as I thought,' said Sheela, getting to her feet.

'What was she in to see you 'bout, ma'am?'

'I'm sorry, officer. I can't go into the details. Privilege, you know?'

'Sure, Ms Murthy, I hear ya. Anything else I can do?'

'Not at the moment, no. But you've been very helpful. Thanks so much for your time, Officer Marlowe!'

'It ain't nothin', ma'am.' He walked them to the door and touched his hat. 'It was an honor to have you in here! Both of you!' he added hurriedly.

Sheela smiled and shook hands on the way out. To her mind, there was nothing much to be done at the moment for Arti Kapoor. At the moment.

***

Thirteen days after Arti Kapoor had first walked into the Law Office of Sheela Murthy, she returned for the second time. One side of her face was purple with bruises, she had a broken wrist and eight stitches on her forehead. Sheela was horrified at the sight of her and rose quickly to ask Aron to join them, when Arti broke down and begged her not to call anybody in. She said that she felt most comfortable with Sheela because she was Indian and a woman like herself.

'Not like yourself,' thought Sheela, vehemently. 'I would never let anybody do this to me. Never!'

Arti told her what happened. Or whatever little she could remember of what happened. Her husband had done it again. She could barely recall how the fight started.

'I think he came home and saw the mail on the table. He said it should have been kept on the cabinet, or something like that. I … I'm not sure what I said to that, but then he … I just can't remember, Sheela. It happened so quickly. One minute we were talking and then suddenly he said … I just can't remember…'

'It doesn't really matter, does it?' asked Sheela quietly, and Arti Kapoor looked up. She shook her head.

'No, it doesn't. Whatever triggers it is always just an excuse to get violent…'

'Shall we contact the women's shelter now?' asked Sheela.

Arti nodded. 'But my green card?'

'Look,' said Sheela briskly, knowing that the time for plain talking had come. 'If this man kills you or causes some irreparable damage to your person, a green card is not going to do you any good. He is counting on your dependence on him for this green card, and that's why he's conveniently abusing you this way. He feels certain you won't leave him as long as he dangles this carrot before you. And till you keep hoping he will get you the green card, he's going to ensure that you never get it because the minute you do, he knows he will lose control over you.'

'So what should I do?' asked Arti in distress, wiping her eyes. 'Should I just return to India?'

'You could. That is always an option. But I'm guessing that it is not what you want, or you would have walked away a long time ago. So I'm assuming that you want to remain in this country but with a green card that you obtain in your own right. Correct?'

'Yes!'

'Then I will help you. But there are some things you will need to do.'

'I will, Sheela. Whatever you say.'

'You'll have to report your husband to the cops. Not tomorrow, not ten days from now but today, while those wounds are still fresh. Next, you will have to check yourself into a women's shelter, where they will protect you and take care of you and ensure that your husband can't contact or harm you again.'

Arti nodded.

Once again she was crying, but this time it was just a steady stream of tears slipping down her face. A look of resolution had come over her now, and she sat up straighter in her chair and met Sheela's eyes as she nodded in agreement. 'Anything else?'

'The main thing. Let me file for your green card. Independently of your husband. Under the VAWA or the Violence Against Women's Act, a woman under circumstances of abuse like yours—if she can prove her case, that is—will be considered for a green card even if she divorces her husband, who is the original applicant and upon whom she has been a dependent this far.'

'Please do it. Please file my papers.' She leaned across the table and extended her left hand, since her right wrist was in a cast. Sheela took it, and Arti smiled. 'Thank you,' she said, and for the first time a smile touched her lips.

* * *

Sheela kept in regular touch with Arti at the women's shelter.

'He tried to contact me, Sheela,' Arti told her. 'But I flatly refused, so they sent him away.' She laughed suddenly. 'I feel so strong and free!' she said. 'Just saying no to him made me feel so powerful! I've never been able to say no to him before, Sheela. *Never!*'

Sheela felt a real sense of satisfaction hearing Arti say those words. She updated her on the filing of the green card, going over the details, and then rang off to get ready for her 2.30 p.m. appointment. Every few days, the two of them spoke over the telephone. On more than one occasion, the husband arrived at the shelter demanding to see his wife, and each time Arti declined to meet with him and he was sent away.

One day, Mr Kapoor stopped coming altogether.

Arti was relieved. She was so relieved, she told Sheela. A few days later, she was, of course, still relieved, only she kept wondering if he was okay. Had something happened to him? Was he ill? Or perhaps he had lost interest in her because he had found someone else?

'I don't think you need to worry about that,' said Sheela firmly. 'Once you have decided to end your relationship with him, it doesn't really matter what he is doing with his time.'

Two days later, when Sheela called the shelter again, she was told that Arti Kapoor had checked herself out and left.

'What do you mean left?' asked Sheela in surprise.

'Her husband showed up here, and this time Mrs Kapoor agreed to meet him. The counselor advised against it but she would not listen. The couple met and spoke for a long time. He convinced her that he was a changed man and would never hit her again. So she left,' explained the woman on the other end of the line. There was a lengthy silence on Sheela's side. Then the lady at the shelter added, 'It's always like this, ma'am. They all eventually fall for the old trick because they never really wanted to leave in the first place.'

Sheela hung up. She was not angry or unhappy—just thoughtful. At lunch that day, Reggie informed her that her 3 o'clock appointment had called to say that she'd be a few minutes late.

'Okay,' said Sheela distractedly. 'Who is it?'

'Arti Kapoor.'

Both Sheela and Aron looked up sharply from their plates at the sound of the name. Two hours later, when Arti arrived at ten minutes past 3, both Aron and Sheela were in the conference room, going over another case. 'Show Arti in here, Reggie, please,' requested Sheela, and when Aron got ready to leave she said, 'Stay, Aron. This won't take long. I know what she is coming in here to say. Once she is done saying it, we can get on with our discussion.'

This time, Arti didn't seem to mind Aron's presence. She looked well, almost joyful, in fact. 'I came to apologize for all the trouble I gave you, Sheela. And for not informing you about leaving the shelter. But I knew you would try to talk me out of it.'

She paused here, probably expecting Sheela to say something. But Sheela only looked back at her calmly and did not respond.

'Er … so, as I was saying, I went back to Saurabh because he's a changed man. He swore he would never do something like that again. I think he really missed me the whole time we were apart, and he's so affectionate now, so caring! It's almost like the old Saurabh never existed!' She paused for a long moment, looking down at her hands. Then, she looked up and said, 'I want you to withdraw my petition for the green card, Sheela. My husband and I intend to file it together very soon. He has already started meeting with his company attorneys. I'm … I'm so sorry I wasted your time. I'm so sorry.'

'Don't worry about it, Arti,' said Sheela. 'It's no problem.'

After Arti left, Aron and Sheela completed their discussion on the Mexican immigrant's case and then Aron stood up and started to leave the room when he turned back. 'Oh, I forgot to ask. So I'll withdraw her petition, then?'

Sheela looked up distractedly from the document she was reading. 'Hmm?'

'The Arti Kapoor green card petition,' he clarified.

'Now, why would we do that?' asked Sheela.

* * *

One morning, when Sheela was scrambling eggs for breakfast, Vasant walked in from the patio with the newspaper in his hand.

'Sheelu, read this,' he said and held out the newspaper to her, folded in such a way as to draw her attention to a particular article.

'Not now, Vasant,' said Sheela. 'I'm running late.' She sprinkled pepper over the eggs and poured in a little milk to soften it.

'Here, let me finish making that. You read this article.'

Handing the ladle over to him, she picked up the newspaper from the kitchen counter and sat down to peruse it. It was an article about medical professionals in the Medically Underserved Area of Appalachia. It outlined the challenges of a few good doctors who had set up practice there, and were struggling against the greed of mining companies and the awful circumstances under which the people in that region lived. And yet, it was an article of hope, for it spoke of how these doctors were fighting to save lives and restore people to health; when they failed to do so, they did everything they could to ease those patients out of life, with as little suffering as possible.

Among the doctors who had been interviewed for this article was one Dr Bashir Abdul Karimi, an Iranian national who had completed his medical studies in the United States. In order to avoid returning to his home country for the mandatory two-year period that his visa stipulated, he had taken advantage of the J-1 Medical Visa Waiver program and worked in the MUA of Appalachia, he told the interviewer.

'At first I thought I'd serve out the term and get away as quickly as possible to begin my life as a doctor,' the article quoted Dr Karimi as saying. 'But after a while, I realized that my life as a doctor had begun the day I arrived in West Virginia. My three-year term of service has long since got over but I never left. I stayed on because the people here need me, and I need them. Every day their presence reminds me of why I chose this profession.'

As her eyes skimmed down the page, the words blurred. Sheela had to keep blinking the tears away. Slowly she looked up from the article to find Vasant watching her. There was happiness in his eyes. She rose from her chair and went into his arms, moved and humbled beyond words, laughing and crying at once.

24

The firm had, for some time now, been renamed Murthy Law Firm, even while it retained its address at 10451 Mill Run Circle, #100, Owings Mills. Only, by this point it had expanded to rent three floors in the plush, ten-floor office building, to accommodate its twenty-four highly competent attorneys. Sheela had selected a fine team of leaders, including Aron, who went on to become Managing Attorney, and three others, Adam Rosen, Pamela Genise and Anna Stepanova, who all became Assistant Managing Attorneys. Although they were non-equity members, the top brass had a considerable say in the management of the firm; they could hire and fire and make policy decisions. There were eighteen associate attorneys who reported to the top management, and about sixty paralegals, who prepared forms and drafted documents, carried out preliminary research and spoke with clients to get a sense of a case before passing it on to one of the certified, bar-admitted attorneys of the firm. The paralegals were not permitted, by law, to render any legal opinion. The firm had policies in place to ensure that.

The name Murthy Law Firm now stood tall and proud on the top of the building, adding its presence to the city's skyline. Some of the attorneys at Murthy Law Firm were members of the American Immigration Lawyers Association (AILA), and regularly attended the monthly meetings of the association. AILA was founded on 14 October 1946, and was a voluntary bar association, a not-for-profit organization which had now grown in strength to over 18,000 members of immigration lawyers and law professors. The association provided continued legal education, information on immigration laws and policies, professional services and up-to-date information in the field of immigration law. The headquarters was at 1331 G Street NW, Suite 300, Washington, D.C. Members of the D.C. Chapter of AILA met on the last Wednesday of every month at different venues across the country's capital, in Maryland or Virginia.

It was Aron's special pleasure to drive down to those meetings along with Sheela. He loved to drive, and much of what he went on to learn from her about immigration law, he learnt from discussions they had on those journeys to and fro. Aron looked forward to those trips eagerly because even though it meant missing an evening with Elisheva and the kids and the family guinea pigs (he honestly didn't know if he missed the kids more or Popcorn and Moose!) it gave him the chance to speak unreservedly to Sheela about cases that had come up during the week or that month, on which he wanted her opinion. As they discussed the more difficult cases at the firm and went over the nuances in the law, he always had her undivided attention and she was able to give him more than opinions and solutions. She gave him insights and wisdom, which he was glad about.

Usually, when Aron returned home after these meetings, he would find Elisheva and their daughter, Rachel, waiting up for him. Over a cup of coffee, he would share with them many of the impressions and ideas that he had picked up from Sheela that evening, before they all turned in for the night. Rachel, who took a keen interest in social work and social issues, was always interested and full of questions. As he sat there in the living room patiently answering them, Aron often felt that working at Murthy Law Firm, despite the formidable pressure that came with the job, brought him closer than ever to his family. Perhaps this was because working at a place where people mattered more than the money had made him more humane.

* * *

On a Wednesday, sometime in mid-2001, Sheela attended a dinner meeting organized by the AILA Washington, D.C. Chapter, for officers from the Customs and Border Protection (CBP). Sheela was excited about this meeting. It would give her and her team the chance to interact with the CBP, and share and exchange information with them.

'What is the CBP looking for, from non-Americans who step off a plane and seek to be allowed into this country?' she asked her lawyers, while inviting them to attend the meeting along with her. 'Surely, someone from the CBP will be the best person to answer that. Isn't it amazing that simply landing in America does not mean that a person has arrived in this country? American soil, for an outsider, begins with that first step they take past the immigration desk. And it is the CBP who are the keepers of that desk. We should interact with them, try to really understand and discover their perspective. It will give us the bigger picture, help us guide our clients better.'

Her enthusiasm and her logic were infectious. It was a novel idea and, many in the room agreed, a very good one. Several attorneys decided to travel the two hours each way from Owings Mills to Washington, D.C., just to interact with the CBP, who had graciously accepted AILA's invitation. So, the following month, five officers from the US Customs and Border Protection arrived at the designated location and hour.

There were close to 200 AILA D.C. Chapter lawyers present at the dinner that evening. Sheela and her team were among them. But as the AILA members milled around talking and greeting each other, fetching drinks and discussing cases, the CBP officers stood by themselves in a corner, speaking in low voices among themselves and feeling completely out of place. Even the executive committee seemed too preoccupied with organizing details for the event to fulfill their duties as hosts.

Sheela observed the state of affairs from her table. She and Aron exchanged exasperated glances a few times at this neglect of the guests, who had come here at the express invitation of AILA. Not a single lawyer in the room seemed interested in using this incredible opportunity to make connections with the CBP officers, whose wealth of knowledge would make a considerable difference in their clients' lives. Aron saw it coming a second before it actually did. He saw Sheela square her shoulders and raise her chin, as if some decision had settled over her, and he knew that things were about to become all right.

Sheela rose to her feet and walked across to the CBP team. She held out her hand to one gentleman and said, 'Hi! I'm Sheela Murthy of Murthy Law Firm. AILA is very pleased and honored that you could take time out from your busy schedule to come and spend time with us this evening!'

The officers brightened instantly because Sheela's warmth was infectious. They introduced themselves, taking turns to shake hands before she led them to her table, where her team of attorneys immediately set about making their guests welcome.

'What will you have to drink?' asked Sheela. Soon the CBP officers found themselves equipped with food and drink, and engaged in conversation. Before long, other AILA members wandered up, drawn to the gathering around the Murthy Law Firm table, and by the lively discussion taking place there. In a matter of minutes, the focus of the entire room became those five officers from the United States Customs and Border Protection. Aron heaved a secret sigh of relief.

The conversation passed quite organically from the MLF table to the podium, when lawyers began to discuss specific cases of clients who had been refused admission into land, sea and air ports of entry around the United States. The CBP team attempted to throw light on the possible reasons behind each, quoting laws and policies that had probably been enforced in those denials. They shared excellent insights into what advice a lawyer could give to the client in order to avoid expedited removals, there being a minimum five-year ban on re-entering the US after deportation.

The discussion turned into a question-and-answer session that involved the entire gathering, and continued for a long time. Both the AILA members and the CBP went away that night with a far better understanding of the actual state of things, and greater sympathy for the challenges and pressures the other had to face on a daily basis. When the discussion was over, the CBP officers returned to the MLF table, and went on to fill their plates at the buffet that had been laid out.

'How can we lawyers help to make your life easier?' asked Sheela earnestly, of one of the officers, Jerry Ficklin, who was seated on her left.

'Stop seeing us as the enemy!' came the prompt reply. Jerry was one of the two Assistant Port Directors present at the dinner that night. He had observed Sheela closely the entire evening and taken a liking to her for her instinctive and unselfconscious kindness to others, her inclusiveness. He had seated himself next to her and spoken with her for a long time, telling her about his wife and children, asking her about her family in India and her year at Harvard.

Val Garcia, another officer at the table, had been Assistant Port Director at John F. Kennedy airport, and had recently been promoted and transferred to the Washington Dulles Airport as Port Director. The lawyers congratulated Val enthusiastically, and joked with him about having to put up with them in the future.

'It won't be easy, I assure you!' said Anna, and Val shook his head in mock dismay.

As Sheela chatted with Jerry, she suddenly asked him a question. 'Jerry, are you sure that it is not you guys who see us as the enemy?'

Jerry frowned. 'What do you mean?' he asked, and everyone around the table paused in their pursuits to listen to what promised to become an interesting discussion.

'I mean,' said Sheela, 'that we AILA guys work predominantly with immigrants. And that perhaps there is a dominant perspective among the Americans about immigrants that may not necessarily be true?'

'Explain,' said Jerry, interestedly.

'When you sit at the immigration desk and screen every person coming through, what goes on in your mind?'

'Er … I don't know. I guess I don't really think…'

'That can't be true. You must have a certain mindset that kicks in when you are working?'

'Yes, coming to think of it, you might be right, Sheela. We probably do, without realizing it,' agreed Val Garcia from across the table. 'That would be part of our job.'

'It would be, yes. Only, there are so many myths regarding immigrants that do the rounds that I wonder if some of it doesn't permeate into the national consciousness? Doesn't it subtly affect the way it all works?'

The others were silent, waiting for her to continue.

'I'm referring to the general misconception that most immigrants are here illegally. Or that their legal entry into this country was easy,' explained Sheela. 'Both are so untrue. Unauthorized immigrants only make up a small percentage of the immigrant population living in the US today. And those who entered legally went through the most rigorous procedures to do so. I should know. I'm here having gone through a screening process that lasted years, and rightly so!'

'Then, there is the myth about immigrants that they take good jobs from US citizens,' interjected Aron. 'Rubbish! According to the American Immigration Council, the real contributing factors to the decline in the number of American workers who are willing to take low-paying jobs are, one, better education and, two, an aging population. It is definitely not because "outsiders are coming in and taking away jobs", as people generally believe they are. In fact, immigrants are coming in because nobody around here is willing to do the job! Despite that, across all industries and occupations, the Americans in the workforce outnumber the immigrants.

'I was reading a report the other day that said that immigrants without authorization are only overrepresented in service, farming and construction occupations because employers often hire undocumented immigrants to fill the void of low-skilled US workers. Apparently, the consequences of this practice are that it is easier for unscrupulous employers to exploit the labor source. They pay below the minimum wage, refuse to provide benefits and side-step worker-safety laws with impunity. But from the economic standpoint, US citizens benefit from relatively low prices on food and other goods produced by undocumented labor,' Aron continued.

'That's terrible!' exclaimed Norma of the CBP. 'I have also observed that in general, immigrants from Muslim nations are eyed with suspicion.'

Anna laughed outright. 'And yet, the annual probability of being murdered by a native-born American is 253 times greater than the chance of dying at the hands of an immigrant. Muslim or otherwise!'

'Look,' said Sheela, 'immigrants come to this country for one or the other of three reasons: to work, to be reunited with family members or to escape a difficult situation—war, persecution, poverty and the likes. Most are couples or are families with children, and they form the work force of the country and contribute considerably to the US economy. Often hailing from poor or even repressive countries, they tend to accept authority, live within their means and are far more willing than Americans to work hard and excel.'

'But does this apply across the board?' asked Norma.

'We come across thousands of immigrants in our line of work, Norma,' explained Anna. 'I mean, that is really what we do, isn't it? And while we don't claim that every single one of them falls into the description, the commonalities truly are striking. Many of our clients keep in touch with us, they come back to us for extensions and renewals and to apply for green cards or they recommend us to friends and family. So we stay in touch and do have an idea of how they are faring in their lives in America. Without exception, even if they haven't become a Steve Jobs, they do have a tough work ethic and raise their kids to excel. They tend not to spend more than they have and prefer to pay upfront for whatever they buy, rather than put themselves in debt.'

'Many of our clients work more than one job, you know?' added Aron. 'When they first arrive in this country, that is often the only way they can make ends meet, and they work two—'

'Sometimes three,' murmured Sheela.

'Yes, three even,' agreed Aron. 'You're referring to Amal Abdallah from Lebanon?' he asked and she nodded.

'And Simran Sharma, Juan Perez, Carmel Santo ... the list is long once you think about it,' said Sheela.

'It is,' agreed Aron, turning back to the CBP officers.

'I guess the point we are trying to make is that the reality of an immigrant in the United States is often very different from the common perspective that people here have of them,' said Sheela. 'They ... *we*, I should say!' she corrected herself with a grin, 'I am an immigrant too, you know. And we help the US economy grow. We are taxpayers, consumers, job creators, entrepreneurs ... we add trillions of dollars to the US gross domestic product. Statistics also show that immigrants are less likely to commit serious crimes than native-born people.'

The officers of the CBP had been listening closely, and Jerry suddenly said, 'You're right. I never really thought about it but we do lead with a certain mindset, buy into the stereotypes, I suppose.'

Suddenly, Sheela had an idea.

'Do you think you could arrange for some of us AILA lawyers to have a private tour of the inner workings of the CBP operation at Dulles airport, Jerry?'

He looked at her for a long, thoughtful moment.

'It is just that we lawyers are officers of the court, you know?' she went on to explain. 'We are supposed to be working together to ensure that only the right kind of people—those who have something good to offer this country and who will genuinely benefit from living here—be allowed to visit or become a part of our American society. And yet, over the years it has become us lawyers versus you, the CBP. Something's not right. I feel if we can come over there and watch how you work, understand your struggles and the challenges you face before putting your stamp on people's passports, we will all be able to start working on the same side.'

There was silence at the table. Suddenly, Sheela smiled. 'In the words of the outstanding lawyer Atticus Finch, you never really know a person until you walk around in his shoes for a while. We'd like the opportunity to walk around in yours.'

* * *

A few days later, the team from Murthy Law Firm, along with a few other AILA members, were taken on a guided tour of the CBP facilities at Dulles International Airport. They got to study, up close, the workings of the CBP.

'There, that is the point where the passengers enter from,' explained Jerry, pointing out the exact area. 'This here is a list of routine questions we ask them. Their answers need to be pretty clear. Often it is purely on instinct that we catch them out.'

It was exciting for Sheela to get the insider's track into the operations, the point of view of the CBP officers—their challenges, perspectives and concerns.

'We have such an impossible and delicate goal to meet,' explained Val, who had taken a few minutes off from work to join the lawyers. 'On one hand, we are the first Americans who welcome people when they land on the US soil. On the other, it is also our mandate to figure the ones who should not be welcomed, should not be allowed inside!'

'They are the keepers of the line that separates the outside from the inside,' mused Sheela silently, as she stood looking at that point of entry where the CBP officers' desks were stationed. It came upon her in that instant that all the ingenuity, the hard work and the struggle that she and her team, and every immigration lawyer across America, put in was for this one instant—when the clients put their foot over that line and walked into America, free!

After all, for an immigration lawyer, it really boiled down to that one fleeting moment, that single crucial act…

The AILA lawyers' tour of the CBP facilities at Dulles International Airport could not have been better timed. Had they delayed it by even a few weeks, they might have missed the opportunity entirely. For, the people of the United States were on the brink of an event that altered America's perception of itself as a nation of immigrants, and turned its face from the 'outsider' with a resoluteness that they would never again relent.

* * *

Four months after Arti Kapoor informed Sheela that she had reconciled with her husband, she returned to the firm. She was in a battered state, and looked almost surprised as she described the gradual but deliberate transformation of her husband from the loving, supportive man he had been after her return from the women's shelter, to the violent, unstable man he had been in the past.

'Have you filed a police complaint against him?' asked Sheela.

'I have,' replied Arti. 'And I have been staying at the women's shelter for a week now. I came here to ask if you would consider filing the green card petition for me once again, Sheela. I know that I will lose many months or years having to wait for it to get approved again. But this time I will not change my mind,' she said.

'There's no need to file again, Arti. I did not withdraw that petition.'

'But...' Arti looked at her in surprise.

'I have dealt with many Violence Against Women Act (VAWA) cases in my career as an immigration lawyer,' explained Sheela. 'And I'm sure this will not be the last, unfortunately. I wish I could tell you differently but not one of those other cases has deviated from the way yours has gone. I know the routine. It is an old routine. A very old one.' There was no gloating in Sheela's words. They were spoken evenly, even kindly, and Arti felt terrible for not heeding her advice the first time.

'If only I had listened to you!' she cried.

'But you couldn't have. If you had, you would have wondered for the rest of your life if you did the right thing by walking out of your marriage. You would have kept thinking that maybe your husband might have changed if you had stuck around a little longer. Now you've been able to see the pattern for yourself, observe how things really are. There is no better teacher than experience. I am only glad that the damage was not any worse.'

'But Sheela, you did all this for me even though I never even paid you!'

Sheela looked surprised. 'You were my client from the minute you walked into my office that first day, Arti. Money had nothing to do with it.'

25

On 11 September 2001, a series of horrific systematic attacks on the twin towers of the World Trade Center in New York and the Pentagon in Virginia shook the United States and the entire world alike. Passenger aircraft were hijacked and flown into the twin towers, razing them to the ground in less than two hours. A third aircraft was flown into the Pentagon, the headquarters of America's Department of Defense. The mastermind behind these attacks was the terrorist group, the Al-Qaeda. The 9/11 attacks (as they came to be known the world over) proved to be a defining moment in the history of the United States. They took America's war on terror to new proportions. National security was no longer confined to the Pentagon but became the all-consuming concern of everybody, including the common public. While the immediate repercussions of the attacks could be clearly enumerated in figures—number of deaths, damage to property and the likes—the traumatized American psyche was the collateral damage that no measuring scale could gauge or predict a limit to.

The Muslim world would bear the brunt of the backlash of the twin tower bombings in times to come.

* * *

In response to the 9/11 incidents and the enormous losses that the nation sustained, Sheela felt that it was time to give back to the two countries that had given her and Vasant their lives and their livelihoods. Within a few months of the attacks, Sheela started the Murthy Foundation—an independent, non-governmental, non-profit organization that she managed to get registered before the end of that year. One of the first things that she did was to set up the Sheela Murthy Travel Grant Endowment at Harvard Law School, her alma mater. The grant paid for professors and faculty of the school to travel, attend and speak at national and international immigration law conferences. This facilitated the exchange of ideas and knowledge with other reputed lawyers in the same field across America and in other parts of the world. The other permanent endowment sponsored by the Murthy Foundation was for an LLM international student who had qualified to be admitted to the program but could only afford to study at Harvard with a scholarship aid. Both endowments are permanent and still on-going.

Some years later, Vasant became a part of the endeavor, and the Foundation changed its name to the MurthyNAYAK Foundation (MNF). Its goal was to better the lives of the poor and the underprivileged—in India and in the United States. MNF largely placed its resources at the disposal of children's and women's health, education and empowerment. It also stepped in to support programs that assisted immigrants, and helped with disaster relief efforts in both countries when the need arose. In India, they worked towards furthering adult education and literacy—a much-neglected area—by offering education and scholarships to the deserving. MNF took upon itself the health, nutritional and educational needs of schools that offered education to children from lower socio-economic groups, directing much of its resources to the improvement and sustenance of orphanages and old-age homes.

The Akshaya Patra Foundation provides hygienically cooked, nutritionally balanced mid-day meals to millions of economically backward school children across India, on a daily basis. The MurthyNAYAK Foundation is a large contributor to Akshaya Patra, among several other organizations and foundations. The Agastya International Foundation, with its sprawling campus situated on the border of three south Indian states, that is, Andhra Pradesh, Tamil Nadu and Karnataka, teaches science through practical innovation and ingenuity to nearly 600 school children every day, both on their campus in Kuppam, Andhra Pradesh, as well as through mobile labs that take science education to children's doorsteps across the country. Children from the small village schools in the neighboring districts take turns to come to the Agastya campus each month to study art, science and design on an ongoing basis. Thus, the Foundation has made huge forays into bringing the finest, most innovative techniques of education to children who might otherwise never have hoped to come into contact with it. The MurthyNAYAK Foundation has involved itself closely in the set-up of the Media Lab at the Agastya campus in Kuppam.

Sheela and the MurthyNAYAK Foundation also went on to become deeply involved with the Girl Scouts of Central Maryland and United Way, contributing generously to their various causes and projects. They have helped to raise funds for the organizations' programs that are aimed at spreading education and helping homeless families, veterans and children from socially underprivileged backgrounds to stand on their own feet. Sheela, generous beyond measure, had the habit of simply pledging her money without a second thought to a cause that genuinely needed it. She led by example and had a light-hearted way of convincing people to follow suit.

Once upon a time, Aron had shared with Sheela what his grandmother used to say to his grandfather every time he tried to save money: 'There ain't no U-Haul behind the hearse!' It was her way of reminding her husband that you can't take your money with you when you die. Sheela laughed so hard when Aron told her this that people had stopped to stare at them as they bought bagels around the street corner. The next time Sheela spoke at a United Way event in Johns Hopkins Hospital, she quoted Aron's grandmother and had people laughing as they donated large amounts of money to the cause. Many who had already given once felt compelled to do better and actually donated a second time. That year, the organization collected more money than it ever had before!

26

Mubarak Haddad was sitting in an aircraft some 37,000 feet over the state of New Mexico, when he felt the need to use the restroom. It had been two hours and some minutes since he boarded the flight at LA. Although he could see that there was a queue of three to four people waiting to use the facilities, he knew that he wouldn't be able to hold on for the remaining two-and-a-half hours before they landed in Baltimore. So he resignedly got out of his seat and wandered up the aisle to wait for his turn, looking around him casually as he did so. The door of the aircraft caught his eye. It was fascinating, with its large knob and tall red arrows. The flight attendant walked past him with a tray of beverages. She was attractive, so he thought he would pass some time by striking up a conversation with her.

'Hey, how you doing?' he asked in his slight Jordanian accent, trying to adopt the nonchalance with which he had heard the Americans toss out this phrase at malls and grocery stores and in movie theaters—basically just about everywhere!

The flight attendant smiled politely and almost walked past him, when he pointed to the door of the aircraft and asked casually, 'How do you work that thing?'

She stopped short, and a tiny frown creased her brow as she looked up at him. 'I'm sorry?'

'Door, door!' he said enthusiastically. 'How do you operate that door?' he mimed turning the knob, smiling at her the whole time. The attendant stared at him, and the frown was replaced by a look of pure terror. Without another word, she marched on ahead towards the front of the aircraft. Minutes later, a voice came over the intercom explaining that due to anticipated turbulence, all passengers were requested to return to their seats immediately and fasten their seatbelts until the captain decided that it was safe to turn off the seatbelt sign once more. Nobody was to leave the seat under any circumstance, not even to use the restroom.

Since Mubarak had been just one person away from his turn, this was something of a blow. 'Ya alqurfa!' he muttered under his breath because now he really had to go. But the attendants were shepherding everybody back to their seats and so he returned to his and sat down. He kept his eyes fixed on the glowing seatbelt sign for the next two hours and seventeen minutes until the aircraft touched down at Baltimore. The sign was never once turned off.

And yet, there hadn't been a single incidence of turbulence the entire journey!

The FBI was waiting for Mubarak Haddad when he deplaned. They seized his Jordanian passport, pocketed it and walked him straight into a room off the side of the immigration booths where they grilled him with questions for hours. He was utterly puzzled and had no idea of what was going on. At last, they took him into custody and grilled him for several days more. Finally, they arrived at the conclusion that because he was on an I-485—Adjustment of Status Pending—his non-immigrant status was no longer maintained. They lost no time in initiating deportation proceedings.

Mubarak Haddad and his wife Salma arrived at the Murthy Law Firm one Monday afternoon in early 2005, in a complete state of panic. One of the junior associates, Jeff, took the Haddad case because that day Sheela, Aron, Anna, and the other members were traveling out of town to attend the Annual AILA Conference. Jeff led the Haddads to the conference room and sat down with them. Stunned by the ordeal of the past several days, Mubarak was silent through the whole meeting. It was Salma who spoke at length, going over in great detail the events that had befallen her husband during his time in custody. As she recounted his story, Mubarak wept silently. Salma held on to his hand tightly the whole time. Badly affected by the grief of the distraught couple, Jeff, not having had many years of experience with such matters, found himself at an utter loss as to how to handle the case.

'Don't worry,' he said to them over and over again, 'You go home and rest. We will find a way to help you.' He sounded far more confident than he felt but at least the couple took solace in his reassurances and went away feeling calmer.

* * *

Every Tuesday, the attorneys at the Murthy Law Firm unfailingly met in the conference room at 1 p.m. to discuss the more challenging cases of the week, and to exchange ideas and solutions. They brainstormed, argued, explained and questioned, and always left the room at the end of the hour with a solution, or at least a multitude of options to present to their clients. That Tuesday, Jeff brought up the case of his Jordanian client and presented the facts as Salma had stated them to him.

'Why did he ask the flight attendant about how to open the door?' asked Aron in surprise.

'She was pretty, apparently,' said Jeff, so earnestly that everyone burst out laughing.

'Fair enough,' grinned Sheela.

'He admitted to this in front of his *wife*?' asked Anna.

'She was the one telling the story. The man just sat there shaking, poor thing. He was traumatized. Apparently, he was just passing the time and struck up casual conversation with the flight attendant. Never thought it would end up in something so enormous! Why did they do this, Sheela? The FBI, I mean?'

'Probably because they are genuinely nervous. They heard a Muslim name and panicked,' replied Sheela. 'After 9/11, we've been seeing plenty of cases like this one, Jeff. And we'll be seeing many more, I suspect. But what is interesting is that in all my years of experience as an immigration lawyer, I have never before seen a case where a person with an I-485 pending was deemed as not maintaining legal status. This one is a first for me!'

In the employment category, to obtain a green card, there are three stages. The first stage is the filing of the labor certification, where the US Department of Labor certifies that there is no qualified and willing US worker to perform those job duties. The second stage is the immigrant petition or the I-140 stage, where the employer petitions for the immigrant worker to work on a permanent and full-time basis for the sponsoring employer. This required the employer to submit their tax returns in order to establish their financial ability to sponsor the individual. At the same time, the individual is required to submit all certificates pertaining to education and work experience. The last and final stage is the I-485—the Adjustment of Status—for those applicants who are already in the US. The individual and the individual's family members need to establish that they do not have a criminal record, any health-related issues or any other grounds of inadmissibility. By this stage, the green card is usually a foregone conclusion, and so the United States Citizenship and Immigration Services (USCIS) routinely approves both the Employment Authorization Document (EAD) and the Advance Parole, which allows the person to freely travel in and out of the United States even before the green card has been issued.

Mubarak Haddad's green card application had reached the I-485, the final stage.

'Never before in the hundreds of cases I've handled has such an incident come up,' Sheela repeated, her brow creased in a thoughtful frown.

'But why did they do it now? Isn't it illegal?' demanded Allison, indignantly.

Aron and Sheela exchanged a quick smile at the righteous anger in her tone. But this is why they had hired her—for her passion and her strong sense of justice. Sheela, like most good leaders, believed that her strength came from surrounding herself with smart, self-motivated, intelligent people. It gave her a tremendous sense of joy and satisfaction that her team at the Murthy Law Firm always had each other's back.

'Actually, it is legal, Allison. It is a gray area, and the USCIS has usually *chosen* to exercise its discretion in the past for those who are in a period of authorized stay. But it is not outside its bounds in doing what it did in the Haddad case. Here, it has merely decided not to use its discretion for him.'

'Sheela, Aron, will one of you handle this one?' asked Jeff, nervously. 'Please? I feel like I'm in over my head here!'

'No Jeff, *you* will handle it. And successfully,' said Aron.

'But *how*?'

'I can see from the glint in Pamela's eye that she already has the answer that I'm about to suggest,' grinned Sheela, pushing the plate of freshly baked chocolate chip cookies across the table to her. Pam helped herself to one—they were her favorite—and bit into it.

'The Writ of Mandamus,' she said.

'What does that mean?' asked Jeff.

'It means we threaten to sue if we don't get an answer.'

'Sue the US Department of State?' he asked.

'Precisely!' said Sheela.

'How does it work and how can we use it in this case?' asked Jeff.

'It is basically a right under the US Constitution that allows a person to sue the federal government in order to demand an answer within a reasonable period of time,' explained Aron.

'Strategically we prepare the entire Mandamus lawsuit package—' began Pam.

'Stating what?' inquired Jeff.

'Stating that our client has been harassed enough, incarcerated, interrogated, mentally traumatized, and can no longer wait indefinitely for an answer,' she explained. 'Usually we don't even reach the stage of filing it. Often, just the threat of a lawsuit against them is enough for the government to reconsider its position and respond favorably.'

Sheela observed Jeff wipe his brow, fiddle with his pen and look away a few times—all signs of his lack of confidence.

'You liked these people, Jeff?' she asked.

'Yes. I felt terrible seeing their distress, and—'

'And you've let your feelings come in the way of handling the case effectively,' she cut across him. Jeff looked up quickly.

'It's a bad world out there,' went on Sheela. 'You'll have to toughen up if you're ever going to make a difference, Jeffery. Because it's going to get worse—a whole lot worse.'

27

In the year 2000, a young man named Senthil Kumar and his wife Suchi moved from their hometown of Salem in Tamil Nadu to Chennai, 215 miles away. Senthil had studied law in Salem, and had later signed up for a course in computer engineering at Aptech—a leading computer software education company. Suchi was his fellow student at Aptech. Over a period of two years, the couple had fallen in love. Suchi's parents would have preferred their daughter to marry a boy from their own community but because Suchi's mind was made up, they got married in a small court ceremony, unattended by any members from her side of the family.

Of course, there were ruffled feathers to be placated, and both Senthil and Suchi felt that the best way to achieve this was to let things settle down at their own pace. If absence did not make the heart grow fonder, it might, at least, soften it! With this hope they left Salem. In Chennai, Senthil Kumar took up a job with a law firm, where he came into contact with immigration law. He took to it like a fish takes to water, and since anyone who was working in the field was bound to come across the name of Sheela Murthy, he too had heard of this legend and was gripped by the idea of a chance to work at the world-renowned Murthy Law Firm. But the idea, fascinating though it was, was equally ridiculous. For, how would a boy from the small town of Salem ever hope to be noticed by a doyen like Ms Murthy, sitting thousands of miles away in Maryland, America! Every time he considered the possibility, the voice in his head laughed out so loudly that he could barely hear his thoughts above the sound of it!

In the meantime, things at his current law firm had grown stagnant and Senthil was frustrated that he was making no progress in his career. The pay was scanty and chances for growth were limited. Senthil took the decision to return to Salem.

'I will practice law with my father there,' he said, filling Suchi with a sense of panic. Return to Salem and face the displeasure of friends and family all over again?

'No, Senthil!' cried Suchi. 'We can't go back. We just can't! I won't be able to live like that, at least not yet!'

'Then what do you want to do, Suchi? There is nothing for me in Chennai. We've been here four years. We've tried everything. Before our twins settle into their lives here, we should move back home and start afresh.'

Suchi was desperate in her mind. But it was true that their twin daughters were still young, and once they grew older it would become harder for them to give up their friends and their school in a bustling metropolis like Chennai, and move back to the relatively quieter life of Salem. And yet, she couldn't bear the thought of giving up so easily. 'What will it take to keep you in Chennai?' she blurted out.

'Nothing,' he replied sadly.

'It can't be nothing. There must be something that you dream of, *something* that would—'

'Working for Sheela Murthy,' Senthil blurted out suddenly. 'But those are not dreams. Those are miracles that don't happen to ordinary men like me.'

'You'll never know unless you try,' Suchi said, catapulting off the bed and fetching the laptop.

* * *

'Sheelu, don't you think this is something you must do?' asked Vasant one night, when they were watching TV before going to bed.

'I don't, Vasant. I have so many clients here at the Owings Mills office, the team and I have our hands full already. What good will it do to have an office in Chennai?'

The city of Madras, where Sheela had completed her undergraduation in history, where Shankar Nayak had studied medicine and Radha Bai had procured her BA degree, had since been renamed Chennai.

'Do you think it will be easy setting up and running an office thousands of miles away in India?' argued Sheela.

'The largest portion of your clients *is* from India. And your workload has nothing to do with an India office, Sheelu, because you will not be running it. We will hire someone really competent to do it for you. It is time to grow beyond the United States.'

Sheela liked the idea of doing good work in India but was concerned about the inordinate amount of effort it would take to set up a new office halfway across the world. She looked at him worriedly.

But her innate trust in Vasant's word and vision instinctively made her consider what he was saying more seriously. After all, her strength as a lawyer had always been her ability to spot potential obstacles to help her clients. Whereas Vasant's, as an artist, was his ability to see the possibilities in the impossible.

An office in Chennai ... was it a possibility, then? Was it really the right thing to do?

* * *

Within a week, the Human Resources Manager at Murthy Law Firm, Owings Mills, responded to a job application submitted by one Mr Senthil Kumar from Chennai, India, giving him the date and time for a telephone interview with Mr Vasant Nayak, who would do the preliminary vetting for the law firm.

The interview took place, and brought with it immediate results. In October 2004, Sheela's first affiliate office, named Murthy Immigration Services Private Limited, was opened in Alwarpet, Chennai, under the leadership and management of Senthil Kumar.

In the coming years, there would be satellite offices in Hyderabad and Mumbai, and a virtual one in Bangalore, which would contribute to the expansion of Sheela's client base and her reputation as one of the finest and best known attorneys in the field of US Immigration Law. Between Sheela and Vasant, Senthil and Suchi, it was to be a long and fruitful relationship. In Senthil, Vasant would find a friend and work partner, a constant companion and helpmate in the many philanthropic ventures MurthyNAYAK Foundation would undertake in the future.

28

One of the reasons for Vasant to quit his job at MICA had been his mother, Radha Bai. He had wanted the luxury of traveling home to India, to spend time with her as often as possible. Radha Bai suffered from poor health and an irrepressible sense of humor, which ensured that despite her constant suffering, those around her never felt weighted down or unhappy.

'It is my karma,' she would say, with the wide, toothless grin that characterized her, and a sparkle in her naughty round eyes. 'Imagine the *terrible* things I must have done in my previous births to have invited all these sufferings upon myself! Nothing comes for free!' and she would laugh so heartily that those around her were grateful that at least she did not suffer over her sufferings.

In those days, Shankar Nayak had been invited to join a reputed teaching hospital, situated on the coast of Karnataka, in an administrative capacity. Shankar and Radha Bai lived in a house not far from the hospital, and as Radha became less and less able to do things around the house, Shankar gradually took over the chores of cooking, grocery shopping and caring for his invalid wife. Alongside, he had been placed in charge of the family planning division of healthcare by the hospital authorities. He traveled from village to village, trying to educate people on the need to adopt birth control methods to limit the number of children they had. In a country that was bursting at the seams with humanity, this was a part of a very essential undertaking by the government.

Shankar was innovative, if not anything. He knew that mere words would never be enough to get through to the superstitious and old-fashioned folks he would encounter in the villages he passed through. And so, he armed himself with a particular painting.

The Birth of Shakuntala was a well-known work of art by a famous painter called Raja Ravi Varma. The picture depicted the story of a beautiful celestial nymph and a great renunciate. In a moment of passion, the sage had entered into carnal relations with the nymph, and this union had resulted in a child. Raja Ravi Varma had painted the nymph holding out the baby to its father, while the sage turned his back on the mother and the child, quite literally. The out-flung arm, the hand thrown up against his forehead, the dramatic twisting away of his body—all depicted energetic rejection of what he perceived as a living proof of his sin.

Shankar Nayak carried a print of this painting from village to village, to remind women that men were always enthusiastic when it came to making a baby but could often quite casually and unconscionably shun their responsibilities once that baby came into the world, thus leaving the mother with the burden of raising and caring for the offspring alone. In some of the poorer sections of Indian society, women were, almost always, the ones who raised the children, went to work and were saddled with the job of bringing home the bacon as well as cooking it. Men often spent their days drinking, sleeping and doing little else. Domestic violence was not unheard of. Given these circumstances, there must scarcely have been a more effective and well thought out ploy to drive home the point of birth control!

Vasant loved and respected his father immensely for the hard-working, determined and dedicated man he was. As for Radha Bai, she was the keeper of his heart. He made it a point to visit them in India as often as he could. As the ability to afford a ticket to India gradually increased, the frequency of his visits from once a year to once every few months became more and more possible. Sheela, who was busier than she had ever been—with her firm, the clients and her rapidly expanding public life—couldn't always accompany him. She also understood, instinctively, that a few weeks alone with his mother rejuvenated Vasant.

Sheela knew herself to be the beloved of her husband. In fact, she realized now that nobody had ever loved her the way he had. After growing up in the environs of her parents' emotionally complex marriage, she had never envisioned anything better for herself. Yet here she was, sharing her home and her life with a man who understood how to love and care for a woman without ever imposing on her dignity or personal space. His love for his mother was part of what made Vasant who he was, and Sheela was glad about it!

She recalled once, during a visit to India, how she had walked into the room and seen Vasant sitting at his mother's feet, talking softly with her. Radha Bai had stroked his hair, as she listened. At that moment, Sheela had seen, for the first time, Vasant as he must have been as a child, through the eyes of his mother. It had moved her beyond anything. Feeling strangely like an intruder, she had turned around and slipped away before the mother or the son could notice her presence in the room.

Sheela shared a warm and affectionate relationship with her mother-in-law. Their mutual love for Vasant seemed to bring them closer to each other, without the slightest sense of jealousy or competition. Radha had never expressed insecurity over Vasant's love for his wife. In fact, she seemed to enjoy and encourage it heartily. To that end, Vasant was never allowed to be impatient with Sheela in his mother or older sister's presence. At any rate, he was not allowed to express it! The one time the poor man made the mistake of doing so, both mother and sister jumped down his throat, and then advised Sheela, much to her amusement, not to stand for any nonsense from him!

So, Sheela had no regrets about Vasant traveling without her.

By 2005, Vasant began to visit India very frequently. It was unclear whether Radha Bai, now in the throes of dementia, even remembered that he had been there once he left. But while he was there, he knew his presence gave her immense joy, and for that reason alone he came to Chennai as often as he could. Chennai was where his parents lived at that time, having moved in with their daughter when Radha Bai's condition became too difficult for Shankar to manage on his own.

Radha Bai now had her daughter, Sheila, with her at all times, and Vasant visiting her once every few months. Shanti and Vijay came down to see their mother once a year. The visits rarely coincided. But it just so happened that on 21 October 2005, Shankar Nayak, Radha Bai and their four children were all together under one roof. That morning, Radha Bai seemed particularly restless. When Vasant and Vijay stepped out for some work, Sheila quickly sent for them, as *Amma* didn't appear well. They hurried back home at once to their mother's bedside.

At the hour of sunset, with her husband beside her and her children gathered around, Radha Bai breathed her last. What had been an arduous life, culminated in a quiet and uneventful death, bringing to an end sixty-five years of love and struggle, quarrels and romance, between her and the man who had stood by her side since they both had been twelve years old. The laughter in those naughty eyes, the irrepressible sense of humor, the outspoken courage and the delicious recipes that was Radha Bai, all came together in a single earthen pot that her husband and children carried with them to the sea, not far from the place she had been born. As they watched her ashes mingle with the salty waters and spread into the ocean, those people who had loved her best in this life knew that Radha Bai was free at last from the suffering she had made so light of. She was unfettered in death, as she could never have been while living. And, amidst the terrible grief and sense of loss, they felt a small stirring of happiness, a semblance of peace...

Three years later, on 6 September 2008, Shankar Nayak followed Radha Bai out of the world. Robust as ever, he had moved from his daughter's home to the house across the street, the one Vasant and Sheela had bought for his use, and which, after his passing, was converted into the office of Murthy Immigration Services. Shankar had moved very shortly after Radha Bai's death; he wanted to live alone and be a burden to no one.

Sheela's affection and respect for her father-in-law had only grown over the years. She helped Vasant and his sister to do everything that they could to make the rancher-style home peaceful and comfortable for him, and Senthil and Suchi stepped in to help whenever there was a need. There was rarely a need, however, because the old doctor remained fiercely independent to the end of his days. He was brisk, lucid, and active till the 4th day of September 2008, after which he came down with a fever. Knowing perfectly well that he had contracted dengue fever from the bite of a mosquito (there was an epidemic in Chennai at that time), and well aware that recovering from it at his age was out of the question, he insisted that his oldest daughter return home and take care of her family, as there was nothing wrong with him. Bred to obey her father's every word, and with the utter faith that Papa could never diagnose an illness incorrectly, she believed him and went home to sleep off the fever that she too had come down with.

By the following day, however, it became apparent that Shankar needed to be admitted to the hospital. A day later, just one month short of his ninetieth birthday, and due to a bite of the tiny and powerful insect that he had battled and subdued so many decades ago, Dr Shankar Nayak passed away quietly in a hospital bed, with only his oldest daughter by his side.

His death marked the end of an era in the life of his children. He took with him their sense of security and their childhood conviction of being protected against every misfortune. What he left behind was an example of unconditional love and indomitable courage, and the legacy of an honest name.

29

This time it was a Lebanese gentleman who walked into the Murthy Law Firm, asking to speak with Sheela. He had entered the United States on a B-2 tourist visa some decades prior. He had stayed on in the country, and eventually found himself a job. He had been working in America without status, which meant that he hadn't applied for the H-1B, out of fear that if he went the legal way, the authorities might deny his application and deport him to his home country. Faud Labaki, the gentleman in question, had fled Lebanon when it was steeped in civil war. He had no desire to return to air raids and bomb blasts at all hours of the day and night, all over again. He had had enough! Thus, having managed to enter the US on a tourist visa, he had quietly remained. It was a case of tourist visa overstay.

Faud Labaki had set foot in America in the mid-1980s, well before the twin tower bombings. At that time, the USCIS (then known as the INS, or the Immigration and Naturalization Service) never used to track these cases too carefully. As he had never left the United States since, his deception had gone undiscovered. So, he had stayed on and earned his bread, and made America his home—far away from the violence that tore at the innards of his home country.

But thereafter, 9/11 had happened. The authorities, shaken out of their complacency, had painstakingly scanned through their database

and dug up a long and convoluted thread of emails connecting a host
of people in America to different corners of the world. Chain mails,
forwards, group emails, everything and anything that had ever been
sent was pulled up and examined with a fine-toothed comb. One
such thread that emerged—forwarded multiple times over to groups
and groups of people—linked Faud Labaki, in a most convoluted
fashion, to a suspect in the 9/11 twin tower blasts.

The FBI appeared on Labaki's doorstep one day and questioned
him for hours. Faud had long since deleted that email. He did not
even remember it; it being entirely irrelevant for having come from
a source he neither knew nor recognized. He told them as much and
begged to be allowed to go to work, since he was already running
very late.

The FBI had left then, and Faud had believed it to be the end of
the matter. Six weeks later, a different set of men, also from the FBI,
were waiting for Labaki when he returned from the grocery store.
They grilled him with the same questions that their colleagues had
bombarded him with before, and the inquisition had lasted for three
hours. The same routine was repeated five weeks later, then again
after eight weeks, until Faud Labaki came to dread returning to his
house for fear of seeing those men in suits and ties waiting for him
at the front door.

'I considered moving house, ma'am,' he told Sheela, 'But I
thought that would make things worse for me. For one thing, those
guys would track me down, and for another it would seem like an
admission of guilt if I ran away. So I stayed.'

'That is correct. You did the right thing,' agreed Sheela.

'One day, while questioning me, one of the agents said, "Mr
Labaki, we have been watching you closely for months now. We've
checked security camera footage of all the mosques in the area and
in the neighboring counties as well but we have never once been
able to find you entering or exiting any of them. Which mosque do
you go to?"'

Sheela sat forward with interest.

"'I don't go to any mosque," I replied. But they wouldn't believe me and I couldn't understand why they wouldn't, until another one of them said, "How can that be, Mr Labaki? How can a devout Arab Muslim like you never go to a mosque?" And I was like "Woah! Wait a minute! What do you mean, devout Muslim? I'm not a Muslim; I'm a Christian! I'm a Maronite Christian."'

Sheela stared in surprise. Her confusion must have shown on her face, because Labaki quickly explained, 'Lebanon has a sizable community of Maronite Christians, Ms Murthy. Didn't you know that?'

'I did,' she replied. 'It's just that my mind never went to that option. I assumed you were Muslim, being from Lebanon. I'm sorry Mr Labaki, I'm not very well-versed with Arab names, and so I just assumed. I mean, just the way you could sit across a table from me and never know by looking at my face what my religion is, I too had the same confusion about you.'

'I understand,' replied Faud Labaki in a low voice, not meeting her eyes. 'People everywhere across the world are like this about Muslims and the Middle-East. I guess nobody is very different after all.' He sounded disappointed and a little angry.

Sheela watched him for a moment and then responded, 'You're wrong, Faud. Sometimes people do not know how to tell the difference because they are ignorant. Others, because it genuinely does not matter to them. It is immaterial to me what your religion is. I would have helped you when I believed you to be Muslim, and now that I know differently, I will help you still. Your religion makes no difference to me.'

He was silent for a minute, and it was an awkward, slightly apologetic silence. Sheela carried on in her pleasant way, as if nothing had happened, 'So what can I do for you?'

Faud Labaki looked up. He replied, in more even tones, 'The FBI never came to my doorstep again, Ms Murthy. A soon as they found out my religion, they never troubled me again. However, a few years have passed, and since then I have met and married a good American woman whom I love very much. I applied for my green card some time ago. It has reached the final stage of processing—the I-485 stage. But now my application has gotten stuck. For years I have waited for a decision. I've asked my immigration lawyer to check with them but there has been no reply from the USCIS. Frankly I don't think my lawyer has bothered to follow up the matter much either. But I do want to know why this is happening to me, ma'am. Why is it this way? They know I am a Christian, they know I had nothing to do with the 9/11 bombings—'

'Who is *they*?' cut in Sheela with a twinkle in her eye.

'The FBI, of course!'

'Of course! But the FBI has nothing to do with your green card petition, Faud. The enquiry about your green card status needs to be directed to the right place—the United States Citizenship and Immigration Services, or the USCIS. Wait, hang on a minute.'

She leaned forward and punched a number into the intercom. 'Jeff? Could you come here for a moment, please?'

A few minutes later, Jeff walked into Sheela's office. He was different now than when he had sat in that conference room a few years ago, fretting over Mubarak Haddad. He carried himself with a new confidence, and met Faud Labaki's eyes with an outstretched hand and a friendly smile, when Sheela said, 'Mr Labaki, this is Jeffery Myers. He's Murthy Law Firm's attorney for filing Writs of Mandamus.'

30

Sheela looked up from the papers before her and said, 'Mrs Mwamba, not only is your I-94 no longer valid but it also has been expired for over a year. This means that you have been out of status for over 365 days now, and that would automatically trigger a ten-year inadmissibility bar. The next time you leave the country, you will not be allowed to reenter it. Not for another ten years at least.'

Grace Mwamba looked at the attorney in real distress. 'How has this happened? I don't understand! All papers were in order. Oteng's papers all in order! I have done nothing wrong, how my I-94 expired?'

Sheela reached forward and patted the woman's hand.

'Don't worry,' she said. 'We will get to the bottom of this. But we will have a better chance of doing that if you can go back to the beginning and tell me what happened, step-by-step.'

Grace Mwamba nodded, drying her eyes and taking a minute to breathe. She sipped the tea that Sheela had set down before her and turned her head to look out of the window through which she saw a large tree, with gorgeous pink flowers in bloom. The sight soothed her overwrought nerves, and soon she pulled herself together.

'Mma Murthy,' she said, addressing the lawyer by the traditional Botswana way of referring to women, 'I go home to Gabarone to attend my niece's wedding last year in January. When I reenter America, I hand my passport and all my documents to the Customs and Border Protection officer at the immigration desk. He enters something into my I-94 and lets me pass through. Many weeks go by. Then one day I discover that the date he has entered into the I-94, it has expired.'

'Yes, I can see that. You are on an H-4 dependent visa. Is your husband's H-1B valid?'

'Valid, Mma. Some time ago it is no longer valid, but now it is valid.'

Sheela felt puzzled by this. She quickly glanced through the documents Grace Mwamba had handed over to her at the start of the meeting.

'Oh,' said Sheela. 'I understand. Your husband's H-1B had expired and subsequently he had obtained an extension.'

'Yes, yes, that is correct,' nodded Mrs Mwamba vigorously.

'It shows me here that your husband's papers are all up-to-date. There is no problem with them. So, when you travelled back from Botswana and re-entered the US, is there any chance that you might have produced his old H-1B before the CBP officer instead of his new one?'

'Er … no Mma, there is no chance of that.'

'Look, Mrs Mwamba, I can see what has happened here. Your husband's old H-1B was still valid when his employer filed his H-1B extension. That is how it is always done, there is always an overlap, it is the correct way. And I can also see here that at the time that you re-entered the country, his old H-1B had not yet expired. So, if you showed that to the CBP officer by mistake instead of the H-1B *extension*, the officer would have accepted it, entered the original H-1B validity date into your I-94 and let you pass through. However, since then, the old H-1B petition has expired. And that is when the trouble began.'

'But I did not show them the old H-1B, Mma Murthy. I show them the new one. I am very sure of that. I carry both and I show both,' said Grace Mwamba, with such earnestness that Sheela believed her.

'You showed them both?'

'Yes, both, both!' insisted Grace, miming holding out two different objects by extending both palms face up to Sheela.

Pointing to her palms, Sheela asked, 'Did you do that? Did you hold out both your hands like that?'

'No, Mma! In my country, not polite to just shove things at other people like that!' exclaimed Mrs Mwamba, shocked at the suggestion. Here, Sheela was hard pressed to suppress a smile, for 'shoving things' at people was *exactly* the way with certain people she knew!

'I have both documents in my right hand,' went on Mrs Mwamba, not noticing the suspicious sparkle of mirth in Sheela's eyes, 'and I hand them over to the officer both together, touching my left fingers to my right elbow while offering it to him. That is polite. That is the way we do it in Botswana, Mma.'

'Was it a busy day?' asked Sheela, suddenly.

'Eh ... I don't understand...'

'Were there many people waiting to clear immigration?'

'Er, yes. Very many, Mma. You see, three flights they land at same time and there is a rush of people waiting to clear immigration. The officer I come up in front of, he is in a hurry.'

'Okay, then that's probably what happened,' said Sheela. 'The CBP officers must have been really rushed and overworked that day. Otherwise they are usually very meticulous about these things. The officer must have opened the uppermost document, which was probably the old H-1B, and accepted it because it was still valid at the time.'

'Oh, Mma! What I do now?' asked Grace, her eyes filling with tears again. 'Oteng's company lawyers, when we consult them, they say to us, they say: "Mr Mwamba," they say, "there is nothing we can do to help you. This is your wife's mistake and we cannot help you. You must file a … a …" something nunc tonk tink, something like that, Mma Murthy. I do not know the name. Nunc tonk ting … sounds of vessels falling down!'

Unable to contain herself any longer, Sheela burst out laughing. Grace Mwamba waited patiently for her to finish. 'You mean a Nunc Pro Tunc!' said Sheela, when she was able to speak again. "Then for Now", it means. They must have suggested that you file an extension with USCIS to request a discretionary Nunc Pro Tunc. But that is completely discretionary. In all likelihood, since it is partly your fault for not being vigilant when the CBP officer was filling in the validity date of the H-1B into your I-94, they will refuse to exercise their discretion in your favor.'

'And if they refuse to do that, then, what happens?'

'You will have to leave the country and be subject to a ten-year inadmissibility bar. A Nunc Pro Tunc is not a good idea, Mrs Mwamba. If you are denied, there is no provision for an appeal once the USCIS turns it down. There is just no reasoning with them,' said Sheela. 'So it is too big a risk.'

'Why did the company lawyer recommend it, Mma Murthy?' asked Grace, aghast.

'Well, you are not their focus or even their client. You're not paying their fees, your husband's company, who is their client, is paying their fees. So they feel that they are only responsible to look out for the company's interest. They would expect you to go to a private attorney for a situation like this and handle this matter on your own.'

'So my coming to you is the right thing!' said Mrs Mwamba, pleased. Sheela felt moved by her simple faith.

'I hope so, Mrs Mwamba. I will do my best. And if I fail, I will not charge you a fee.'

'But what are you going to do, Mma?'

'I am going to ask my attorney, Mr Aron Finkelstein, to accompany you to the Dulles Airport and meet the CBP officer there. He will explain the error to CBP and request them to issue a correction of the expiry date in your I-94.'

'*You*. You come with me to the airport,' said Grace firmly.

'Aron is Murthy Law Firm's Managing Attorney. He handles all communications with the CBP, Mrs Mwamba. He is the best person for this job because he knows people there and they trust him. It is on his assurance that they might consider making this correction.'

But Mrs Mwamba shook her head resolutely and said, 'No, Mma. I want only *you* to come with me.'

* * *

'Murthy Law Firm. That is correct. Ms Sheela Murthy would like to come in and meet with an officer at CBP, please,' clarified Reggie. 'She will be coming in herself for this meeting.'

The officer on the other side noted this down and gave Reggie the date and time when the CBP office would be open for such matters. Three days later, Sheela accompanied Oteng and Grace Mwamba to the Dulles International Airport, and made her way to the CBP area. It had been fifteen years since she and the other AILA attorneys had visited this very place for the guided tour that the CBP had so graciously given them all. There might have been more such interactions. But, when the twin tower bombings had taken place on 11 September 2001 just weeks after that guided tour, the government had tightened security and put a stop to non-airport personnel having that kind of access to the airport premises, particularly in places as sensitive as the CBP work areas. Yet, somehow, despite the passing of so many years, the area felt so familiar to Sheela as if she had visited just yesterday...

A junior officer stepped out to meet her and the Mwambas, and asked them to please be seated. They waited by themselves for some minutes, the couple looking tense and terrified at the gargantuan consequences that a possible rejection from the CBP could have on their lives.

'We will go home, Grace,' Oteng had said in Setswana as he had held his wife consolingly the previous night. 'If Mma Murthy is unable to help us, if the CBP refuses to admit that they might have made a mistake, if they refuse to correct it, then we will pack our bags and return to Botswana.'

This was not easy for him to say. His job as a professor at the University of Maryland was very important to him. He had his work, his students, the research grant he was in charge of … letting go of all those things would be a terrible blow to his aspirations and his career. But poor Grace, she had been beating herself up over her carelessness for not checking the validity date on her I-94. Over and over she had said, 'If only I glance at it even for one second instead of just closing my passport and walking away! Now I have ruined our lives with this one stupidity!' Oteng knew that his wife had stopped sleeping at nights and was barely touching her food because she had been so worried and unhappy since the discovery of the expired I-94.

'No, Oteng,' she had replied seriously to his suggestion. 'We will do no such thing. I will return to Botswana and you will stay on in America. You will visit me but you will not quit your job and return home. No!' she had cried when he tried to interrupt. 'I will not allow it and that is final!'

But they both knew that living apart in two separate countries for ten whole years, or maybe more, was not something that they would be able to manage. It would be too great a suffering.

* * *

The door of the cabin opened, and Sheela looked up. She blinked, unable to believe her eyes. Jerry Ficklin was standing there, beaming down at her.

'*Jerry?*' she asked in disbelief.

'Someone else was supposed to handle this meeting. But when I heard it was you who were coming in today, I just had to say hello in person! Sheela, how are you?' he said, and stepping forward, brushed aside her extended hand and said, 'It's been fifteen years. I'm not going to shake hands. I'm going to give you a hug!'

Sheela was thrilled to see her friend again, touched by the warmth of his manner when he stepped back and exclaimed that she looked exactly the same as the last time he had seen her, and that she hadn't changed one little bit! As she surveyed him, however, she realized that the years had not been kind to him. He looked much older than his sixty-odd years, and there were dark circles under his eyes. Only his smile, she was happy to note, was as youthful and energetic as ever.

'What is the matter, Jerry? Have you been ill?' she asked in concern.

'Aw, it's nothing! The doctors are just giving me a hard time 'cause that's the way they scare us!' he chuckled, and Sheela was half-convinced. They immediately got down to business. Sheela began by explaining the details of what had transpired on that busy afternoon at the immigration desk, the previous January—on the day that Grace Mwamba had re-entered the United States. Jerry listened attentively to her. Then, she gave him her word that she had personally confirmed, beyond a shadow of doubt, that Mrs Mwamba had handed both Oteng's old H-1B as well as the more recent H-1B extension to the CBP officer. Once she said this, she realized that Jerry was no longer listening to her. His attention was on the document before him. She glanced down and saw that he had made the correction to the date. He had struck off the old, expired date in Grace's I-94, written in the new validity date, and stamped it. All because of Sheela's word. Just on her word.

Sheela had encountered numerous people, made countless friends in her years in America. But this man, Jerry Ficklin, who had known her briefly many years ago, had put his faith in her so simply. It was a happy moment for Sheela, and a humbling one.

* * *

Three months later, as Sheela sipped her tea and checked her morning emails, she came across one from AILA announcing the death of Jerry Ficklin, a valued and trusted member of the US Customs and Border Protection team. What had seemed like a happy coincidence—the Mwambas, the visit to the CBP, the fact that she had gone in Aron's place and the meeting with Jerry—now became clear to Sheela for what it really was: an opportunity to say goodbye to an old friend.

31

Sheela's one regret, probably the only one in her happy, bustling life, was that she didn't have the time to visit Daddy as frequently as she would have liked to. She tried to compensate by making it a point to finish every day, no matter which part of the world she was in, with a phone call to him. She never went to bed without hearing his voice. And yet still, she felt it was not enough.

Being the favorite among his three daughters, she knew he waited for her to come home to India. She noticed in particular, that whenever she visited without Vasant, her father all but abandoned his room downstairs and came up to spend every minute of the day with her—talking, laughing and sharing all sorts of stories. One day, halfway through a discussion, she had got up to use the restroom. When she came out, she realized that her father, Colonel Murthy, had been chatting incessantly outside the door.

'Daddy! What are you doing here?' Sheela had exclaimed, and Colonel Murthy had looked as surprised as she had been to find himself standing there. They had both burst out laughing!

Colonel Murthy confided in Sheela all about his losses at the card table, and the business ventures he undertook to help out his friends, which, unfortunately, always ended in him sinking his own money! These were things he *could* never share with Indu, and *would* never share with his other two daughters, dear though they were to him. Suman visited often enough from Mumbai where she had settled down, and Shree had moved back into the house with Colonel and Indu Murthy after her divorce, bringing her little daughter with her. Colonel Murthy adored the child and took special care of her. But Sheela was Sheela, and nobody could ever take her place in his heart.

Colonel Murthy told Sheela about the charities that he and his friends liked to contribute to through an association of retired army officers that they had formed, called the Senior Citizens of Bangalore. And Sheela, longing to make her father's remaining years in this world happy and content, paid up his debts without ever letting her mother know. She made good his losses, and generously donated to the charities that were dearest to his heart. Through the MurthyNAYAK Foundation, she adopted a school for the children of construction workers and paid for their education, nutrition and uniforms. She also provided financial help to an old age home that the Senior Citizens of Bangalore supported.

Sheela knew it made Daddy happy and proud that his darling daughter was earning well. But she knew it would mean even more that she shared her wealth freely with those who needed it. After all, it was he who had taught her to do so.

Lakshmi, the young girl who used to clean the Murthy residence when Sheela had first left for America, had since grown up and married. She now had a daughter of her own. Her husband, a wastrel, had abandoned her and her little child. And after a four-year-long hiatus from house-cleaning work, Lakshmi had returned to the Murthy residence—alone, penniless and frightened. Clear in Sheela's memory was that distant day when Daddy had pointed to little Lakshmi mopping the floor. The words he had spoken still rang in her ears, wishing her wealth and success in her career, but cautioning her to share that prosperity with others so that they too would be able to come up in life. Those words were as fresh in her memory as the day Daddy had spoken them, and Sheela watched Lakshmi's child hang onto her mother's legs as Lakshmi went about her work.

'How old is she? Sheela had asked suddenly.

'Six, *akka*.'

'Doesn't she go to school?'

'I can't afford to send her,' mumbled Lakshmi, embarrassed.

'Then I will pay for it.'

The very next day, Sheela had taken the little girl to a reputed school nearby, where the medium of instruction was English. While there are undeniable advantages in studying in one's own mother tongue, Sheela felt that the child would benefit from an education that would put her on par with children from every corner of the country, and from every stratum of the society. Sheela hoped that someday, Lakshmi's little girl would have a life that was better, much better, than the one her mother had experienced so far.

* * *

Back in Ownings Mills, one day in the fall of 2014, Sheela was in the middle of an unusually busy day. There had been back-to-back appointments with clients and some of the cases had been difficult. It had been one of those days that had stretched out interminably, and by the time she and Vasant had washed the dinner dishes and put the food away, Sheela was so exhausted that she was almost tempted to go to bed without her customary phone call to Daddy. Only, the previous night when she had spoken to him, he had seemed unlike his cheerful, optimistic self. He had spoken at length of Mandolin Srinivas, the world-famous, forty-five-year-old mandolin maestro, who had died just six days prior, of complications following a liver transplant.

'That boy was a teetotaler, a vegetarian and a non-smoker his entire life, Sheela!' her father had exclaimed sadly. 'A death sentence from a liver disease in one so young and with such an illustrious career ahead of him just seems so terribly unfair. It doesn't make any sense!' Daddy had lamented, repeatedly the past few days, every time she had spoken with him. This was very unlike him, a man who had always been philosophical about death. Besides, it was not in Colonel Murthy to dwell on morbid subjects for so long. He was just too sunny-natured and easygoing for that. But when, last night, he had said, 'Why should a forty-five-year-old boy be taken away from the world while an eighty-four-year-old man like me is being allowed to live?' Sheela had grown alarmed.

'Daddy, you're eighty-three, not eighty-four, and stop being dramatic!' she had scolded in her no-nonsense way, trying to fight down the strange sense of foreboding his words had filled her with.

'I have no fear of death, Sheela,' he assured her. 'I have three lovely daughters, two beautiful granddaughters and sons-in-law. I must have done a great deal of good in my previous birth to have got all of you in this lifetime. My youngest child is three months away from turning fifty. What more can a man ask for from life?'

'Daddy, stop it. Just stop talking this stuff. I'm coming there next week and I'm going to stay for awhile. We'll have plenty of time to discuss all this—'

'When you come, we will discuss the finances and settle some property matters as well, Sheela,' he had said. Then, slowly, he added, 'I am looking forward to having you with me again, my child.'

Sheela found herself blinking back tears at the love in his voice. For a while now, she had wanted to return home and spend uninterrupted time with Daddy. She had worked towards this— systematically delegating firm responsibilities, wrapping up whichever cases she could, handing over the pending ones to Aron and Anna and declining all social appointments for the coming weeks, in order to be able to take time off from work. At long last, she had been able to pull it off. She was due to travel to India very shortly, and stay on for a few months. She was really looking forward to it. But not, she suspected, as much as Daddy was!

That night, despite her exhaustion, Sheela picked up the phone and called. Mummy had gone to attend a three-day yoga camp somewhere on the outskirts of Bangalore, and Sheela wanted to make sure Daddy was alright by himself (Shree would be busy with her patients) before she turned in for the night.

It was morning in Bangalore, and father and daughter had a brief but reassuring conversation before Colonel Murthy insisted Sheela go to bed. Before he put down the phone, he said, 'I love you,' as always, and then added, 'God bless you, Sheela.'

* * *

The Secretary of Senior Citizens of Bangalore came over to the Murthy residence in Indiranagar to discuss some matters of the organization that morning. It was an unhurried, two-hour-long conversation, in which Colonel Murthy managed to apprise the secretary of various aspects of the work that he had been handling that far. After the gentleman left, Colonel Murthy took a shower and then had an early lunch. He was looking forward to his friends coming over for his favorite cards game of Rummy that afternoon.

'Daddy?' said Shree, poking her head around the door.

'Yes?'

'I'm going over to the Indiranagar Club. I'll be back in an hour or so.'

'Okay, Shree. I'll be upstairs by the time you get back. I'm expecting Srinivasan, Gupta and Sheshakumar.'

'Should I have Priya send up some snacks and tea?'

'Would you?'

'Sure. I'll tell her. Bye Daddy, I'll see you in a little while,' said Shree.

Shortly after Shree's departure, the retired army officers—Colonel
Murthy's card-buddies—arrived. He sent them on upstairs, fetched
his spectacles and followed. A couple of minutes later, Priya, the
house help, loaded the tray with biscuits, tea and snacks, and prepared
to take them to the guests.

It was 2 o'clock in the afternoon, on 25 September 2014.

* * *

In the wee hours of the morning in Owings Mills, the telephone on
Sheela's bedside table rang. Disoriented, she reached to answer it,
while Vasant sat up sleepily.

'Sheela...' came Shree's voice down the line, and she was weeping.
'Daddy... Daddy...' was all she could say after that, over and over
again. Sheela's heart went cold. Vasant knew at once that something
was wrong, and took the phone from her hand.

'He collapsed as he was going upstairs to join his friends, Vasant,'
sobbed Shree, when she was able to pull herself together, enough to
be able to speak. 'Priya found him lying there at the foot of the stairs,
and she tried to wake him. She called me at the club and I rushed
back. Meanwhile, his friends had carried him and put him on the
bed. By the time I got home, he was gone. There was nothing we
could do for him, Vasant!'

Daddy is dead. Daddy is dead. The words rang over and over in
Sheela's numbed brain. But Daddy? How could he be dead? What
would become of laughter and kindness, silly jokes and foolish
anecdotes, and snotty noses wiped secretly on the undersides of shirts?
What would become of childhood and home, if Daddy went away?

Sheela didn't cry. As she felt Vasant's arms go around her, she knew
that for the first time in her life, something so terrible had happened
that tears would not be enough to contain the enormity of it.

* * *

The wild horses on the pristine white beach of Assateague Island were beautiful. They ran alongside the car for miles and miles, while the grey skies overhead bent low into the Atlantic, as if reaching down to embrace it. Vasant drove on, while Sheela sat beside him, silent and dry-eyed, looking upon the beauty of the place with eyes that didn't see.

'One day it will be okay, Sheelu,' said Vasant at last. 'One day you will look down at your hands, your feet, and suddenly know that his blood continues to flow in them. Every time you give money away to someone who needs it or are kind to a fellow human being, it will be his kindness and generosity expressing itself through you. Some people never die, Sheelu.'

She turned her head and looked at him for a long time. 'How do you know?' she asked, her voice rusty and weary.

Vasant smiled sadly and replied, 'Because I do.'

32

'It's going to get worse,' Sheela had said to Jeff one distant day in the past. 'A whole lot worse.'

Prophetic words, those turned out to be. For, very early in 2017, a man entered the White House, losing the popular vote by about three million votes but winning the Electoral College, to turn the world upside down on its head. The blow was sharper, for he followed on the heels of a mighty-hearted President who, during his two terms in office, brought an end to the American wars with Iraq and Afghanistan, and presided over a dangerous mission that resulted in the death of Osama bin Laden, the mastermind of the 11 September 2001 terrorist bombings. The office of the President of the United States of America had historically carried with it the connotations of being the global leader, the protector of the underdog, the head of the world's last remaining superpower—and never more so than under the leadership of President Barack Obama.

The new President, on the other hand, in his very campaign speeches, redefined that role. In particular, his attitude towards immigrants—illegal and otherwise—would have life-changing repercussions on people all over the world.

Prior to this, in its twenty-three years of existence, Murthy Law Firm had been used to over 99 per cent approvals with their H-1B petitions. This was so even after 9/11. The year 2017 ushered in a new era in the history of the law firm. Petitions that did not require more than a few hours to review, as simple and straightforward as extensions of status that were usually mere open-and-shut cases, now languished for months with the USCIS, often resulting in a Request for Evidence (RFE) or worse, a denial.

The Writ of Mandamus that had got Mubarak Haddad, Faud Labaki and hundreds of other clients of the firm their green card approvals within a few weeks of being filed, now no longer worked with the old speed and efficiency. Where the government had once expedited their decisions on the mere threat of a law suit, they now sat back and allowed the cases to go to the courts, lengthening the waiting time immeasurably, and costing the applicant and the tax payer hard-earned money and precious time.

The firm now faced between fifteen to twenty per cent denials, especially with H-1Bs. Even though the average rate of denials with other immigration law firms was much higher, these statistics brought the attorneys of the Murthy Law Firm no pleasure. Indeed, they came into work each morning with a grim sense of foreboding in the pit of their stomachs. This had been the case ever since things had gone downhill with Naila Omar Pasha of Kenyan origin.

Naila had been one of Sheela's long-standing clients, and had come to the United States from Nairobi to complete her MS at Rutgers University, some ten years prior. Thereafter, she had done her STEM OPT—a 24-month period of temporary training that directly relates to an F-1 student's program of study in an approved STEM field— and then found herself a very good job. She was well-educated and intelligent, and Sheela had come to respect and admire the young woman for her courage and sense of fairness.

'I will not stay in this country for free and drain its resources, Ms Murthy,' Naila had told her. 'I know what it is to live in poverty, with the threat of hunger hanging over my head all the time. I want my life in America to be one of honest hard work and honor. America should be proud to have me here. I want to give back to this country for taking me in when I needed a home.'

Sheela's heart had lifted with joy as she had looked at the beautiful face before her, with its dusky skin, classical features, proud cheekbones and liquid, almond-shaped eyes—so typical of the Kenyan Arab women.

Prior to her advent to the United States, Naila had married a man who she had grown up with in Mombasa, and loved nearly all her life. It had been a happy marriage. Omar Pasha and Naila had two daughters, Mariam and Aidah. At the time that the family had first moved to the United States, both girls had been very young. Prior to the move, during her student years, Naila had traveled back to Kenya once a year to visit her family, where Omar worked and took care of his daughters with some help from Naila's mother. Once Naila had got a job in America, and her H-1B status had been approved, Sheela had helped her file for the H-4 dependent visas for Omar and the two girls. The H-4 visas had come through without a hitch, and Omar, Mariam and Aidah had joined Naila to start a new life in America. Since then, Naila had obtained prior H-1B approvals at the Murthy Law Firm multiple times over the years. Sheela and Naila, both immigrants and women of color, had forged a bond of friendship and understanding based on shared experiences of hard work and a mutual love for their adopted country.

Then, in January 2017, almost overnight, with no changes in the immigration laws or issuance of any regulations in majority of the cases, based solely on policy changes, H-1B extensions began to be denied right and left.

That year, for the very first time, Naila's extension was denied and Murthy Law Firm went into overdrive trying to save the situation. Sheela, Aron and Pam put their heads together to come up with any possible legal solution in the book.

'The USCIS has no grounds to deny her extension petition!' cried Pamela Genise. 'What they are doing is in clear violation of the law!'

Sheela said nothing but remained at the office late into the night, trying to explore if there was any angle to the case that she had missed. Two of the paralegals, knowing how important the case was to her, volunteered to remain past work hours and help. The three worked through the night, and in the morning, they found themselves frustrated, disgruntled and no closer to a solution.

The Murthy Law Firm's legal team had already filed the MTR, or Motion to Reconsider, and also filed a new H-1B petition through the employer for Naila. However, both had been denied based on presumed lack of specialty occupation—the very grounds upon which she had first procured her H-1B—even though there had been no change in her job duties and line of work in the past ten years. How the requirements for specialty occupation could change overnight when there had been no new laws or regulations remained a mystery. Sheela suggested filing a lawsuit, as in the firm's experience, the USCIS often buckled when they realized that they could lose in a court of law. However, Naila and Omar wanted nothing to do with suing the federal government. They were concerned about possible retaliation. They felt that they should remain in America only if they were considered valuable contributors to the US economy, and not otherwise.

With all options exhausted, Naila, Omar and their daughters would have to leave the United States. Omar had been working in the country on an H-4 EAD—the Employment Authorization Document that allowed a dependent to legally work in America. His H-4 EAD would never be renewed now that Naila's H-1B extension petition had been denied. The girls, both at crucial stages of their academic lives, would have to be withdrawn from school. The house, the cars and all the assets would have to be sold, and the beloved family dogs—Toto and Kidogo, whom Naila had so often spoken about to Sheela—relocated to foster homes. The impact on the Pasha family would be devastating. After living and working in the US for over a decade, Naila would have to be informed that she was no longer wanted in the country she loved and had worked so hard to give back to.

Sheela knew, as nobody else did, that Naila routinely took her daughters with her to volunteer at their local hospice and at the women's shelter, to keep the promise she had made to herself of giving back to the country that had taken her and her family in.

For the first time since Daddy passed away, Sheela sat alone in her office in the wee hours of the morning, put her face in her hands and wept. After a while, she wiped her tears, picked up her briefcase and went home. It would be a new day at work when the sun came up. She would return to fight for the next client and the next, and she would keep on fighting despite the harsh and negative climate the country had plunged into. For, there was one thing that Sheela believed in, above all things.

Hope.

* * *

Senthil sent an urgent message to Amanda that a young man named Ravi Kumar had come into the Murthy Immigration Services office in Chennai, asking to speak with Sheela.

Senthil had tried to explain to him that Sheela only visited the liaison office a couple of times a year, and the rest of the time operated from her office in Baltimore. He had asked if he could be of help but the man had looked distraught and insisted that nobody could help him except Sheela Murthy.

'Senthil wants to know what to tell this guy,' said Amanda Howdyshell, her new Executive Assistant, who had joined the firm in June 2018, when Reggie had left to get married.

'Tell him I'll speak to Ravi Kumar over the phone. Give him an appointment, Amanda. Just keep in mind that it can't be anytime in the middle of the working day because India will be sleeping at that time. They are about nine-and-a-half hours ahead of us.'

'But then it will mean you taking the call at home,' said Amanda hesitantly.

'That is not a problem!' replied Sheela briskly, and returned to perusing the file on the couple from Honduras.

By 8.30 p.m., Eastern Standard Time, Sheela and Vasant had washed the dinner dishes and put away the leftover food in the fridge. Sheela was then ready to take Ravi Kumar's call.

'M ... Ms Murthy, ma'am?' came a nervous voice down the line.

'Hi Ravi, this is Sheela! How can I help you?' she asked so pleasantly, that the young man was immediately put at his ease.

'It's so great to finally talk to you, ma'am! I was so desperate! Thanks for taking the time out to help me,' he said earnestly.

'That's what I'm here for, Ravi. Tell me, how can I help you today?'

Ravi Kumar's passport had been languishing at the American Consulate for months. When he had first entered the United States, it had been on an H-1B visa from his former employer. Since then, he had found a new job in the US. The Change in Employer Petition for the new company had been approved.

'So you joined the new company based on a USCIS-issued H-1B petition approval?'

'That's right, ma'am.'

'Please call me Sheela,' she said absent-mindedly and then went on. 'Did it have the I-94 card attached to it?'

'Yes, it did, ma'am. I mean, Ms Sheela!'

'So you had valid legal status in the US to live and work here. Okay, go on,' she urged, then added quickly, 'Never mind, I know what happened next. You left the country—'

'To attend my sister's wedding, yes.'

'—and when you tried to re-enter it, you were asked to apply for a fresh H-1B visa, right?'

'That's correct. I'm not sure why I needed to do that, though. After all, I have my I-94…'

'The H-1B status is different from the H-1B visa, Ravi. Status is issued by the USCIS and gives you legal permission to live and work in the US. But a visa stamp is issued by the American Consulate in a person's home country, and is what you need to *enter* the United States every time you depart the US. So, did you apply for the fresh H-1B?'

'I did. Three months ago! The consulate had issued several questions despite my having the I-94, and they have decided to reopen my case and review each and everything from scratch! They have not issued the visa and neither have they returned my passport.'

'What about your job back in the US?'

'They are threatening to terminate my employment. I had only just joined a few months prior to leaving for India, and I don't have much goodwill with them yet, Sheela. At this point, I'm just another employee. Just another *dispensable* employee, it turns out, because even the company lawyer told me quite curtly that there is little she can do to help me.' A note of bitterness had crept into his voice. 'In the meantime,' he added, 'I have had to continue paying the $1,300 rent for my apartment in Boston.'

'What kind of information is the Consular Officer in Chennai seeking from your employer and you?' asked Sheela.

'They want the company's tax returns, a list of all the other employees in the company along with their salaries, my pay stubs from the time I started at the new company and my W-2 (year-end taxes) from my previous job.'

'Hmm. They are hoping to find evidence to indicate that you are out of status.'

'Meaning?' asked Ravi.

'In order to remain in the US, it is essential for a person to apply and get status—work status, dependent status, permanent resident status, whatever. But it is also important for that individual to maintain that status, which means that they continue to deserve it by meeting certain criteria. Paying taxes is one of them. Being employed is another. Being employed by a company that can afford to pay you and its other employees is a third. In this case, the consulate wants to know if your employer has the ability to pay the salary they have promised. If they don't then they have violated the law, but it also means that you have failed to maintain status. That could become possible grounds for denying you a visa. There is a fear that a foreign national can be exploited, where an American company tries to procure cheap labor by promising a higher salary on paper but actually pays that foreign national less money. In many cases, the foreign national will agree to this kind of chicanery in exchange for being able to live in the United States. So, the US Government tries to keep a close eye to monitor such possible situations.'

'They never asked for all these documents when we filed the petition for the fresh H-1B through my new employer!' exclaimed Ravi indignantly.

'But this is for the *visa*. The information required for visa issuance can be different. They are looking for the information you submit now to corroborate the information you submitted for the H-1B petition back in the United States.'

'It was so simple at that time, though. Even the first time I got my visa, which was two years ago, it all happened so simply. Why are they making this so hard? Have the laws changed?' asked Ravi, sounded puzzled.

'The laws are intact,' replied Sheela grimly. 'It's the policies that have changed. The way the government wants them to be *interpreted*, that is what has changed.' She spoke the words softly but the import of them carried the impact of a whiplash.

'Tell me, what did your company lawyer advice?'

'Nothing.'

'Nothing at all?'

'No, ma'am. They're ready to throw up their hands. They and all the other four immigration lawyers I consulted after them!'

Sheela said nothing for a long time, and Ravi interrupted with a tentative, 'Sheela…?'

'Give me a minute,' said Sheela. 'I feel like we're missing something here. But I'm not able to put my finger on exactly—'

'On exactly?'

Suddenly, and despite the thousands of miles separating the two, Ravi felt something shift on the other side of the line. The energy had shifted to the kind that comes with forethought, a pre-knowledge of something, even before it has had the chance to manifest as material certainty.

Ravi went still, waiting for Sheela's next words, which he knew would be the turning point in his case.

'When did your previous visa expire?' she asked with almost deceptive calm.

'Er … expire?'

'Yes, expire.'

A feeling of disappointment shot through Ravi. This was not a question he was expecting. What sort of question was that? How did the answer matter, anyway? 'I don't … that is…' he seemed to be wracking his memory. 'I don't think—'

'—that it has expired?' she finished for him, but she already knew the answer, for there was a note of satisfaction in her voice.

'I still have another two months on it,' said Ravi. 'But then I thought that it would no longer be valid now that I have quit the old company.'

'But it is *completely* valid to legally enter the US when produced along with the H-1B approval for your current employer. Was this question never discussed by any of the other lawyers you had consulted?' asked Sheela.

Ravi was silent. Flashing through his mind were the thousands of dollars of legal fees that he had spent on advice that had brought him no solutions, the sleepless nights he had spent in those past three months, fretting over the rent on his American apartment that he could no longer afford to pay, the ultimatum from his company to terminate his services if he couldn't get back to work immediately, and so on.

'Look, Ravi,' went on Sheela, 'this is only a way of addressing the immediate crisis and postponing it for a little while. The next time you leave America and need to re-enter, you will have to apply for a fresh visa, and the same questions will be raised. At that time, once again you run the risk of your visa being delayed or denied. So, this solution that I am giving you is only a stop-gap—'

'I do not intend to leave America again, ma'am. Not until I have my permanent resident status.'

'Or, at least till your green card reaches the stage of Advance Parole, which will permit you to freely travel in and out of the US without a visa,' advised Sheela. 'But for now, here's what I suggest. Request the consulate to return your passport. Use your old visa stamp with your prior employer along with the new H-1B approval notice from the current employer, and return to the United States. I suggest that you to fly Etihad Airways because Abu Dhabi is now one of the legal ports of entry into America. Pre-flight inspection happens there, and once you're cleared, you will know that at the end of your long and expensive flight to Boston, your entry into America will more or less be a certainty. At Abu Dhabi, use the documents I told you about, to clear immigration.'

On the other side, there was silence. Sheela realized that Ravi Kumar was trying to say something but couldn't.

'Ravi,' she said, 'it's time to get back to work.'

* * *

Sheela pulled an all-nighter that night. Having spoken with Ravi and brought his case to a satisfactory closure, she knew that there was nothing more to be done from her end until he called her back—hopefully from an American number.

Now she turned her attention to the case of the Honduran couple. She went through the file she had been reading when Ravi Kumar called, starting from the beginning and reading all the way to the end. Anna had been meticulous, as always, in the presentation of the case and Sheela felt a warm sense of gratitude for this team of lawyers that she had been blessed with. They were her greatest strength. While the world may praise her, Sheela Murthy, for her success in solving difficult immigration cases even in these troubled times, she knew that her accomplishments today had much to do with the attorneys and staff at Murthy Law Firm, who worked intelligently and skillfully behind the scenes. She knew her success had so much to do with them, and with Vasant. Always Vasant.

Pamela had expressed, a while ago, that she needed to quit her job at Murthy Law Firm and move out west to be closer to her parents. 'They're growing old, Sheela,' she had said one day with a catch in her voice. 'It just doesn't work anymore, me being here in Baltimore so far away. I hate the thought of leaving, MLF, you know? But…'

And Pamela stopped speaking for a minute because the thought of not being a part of the MLF family almost overwhelmed her.

Sheela watched Pam silently the whole time that she spoke. Unbidden, came the memory of one summer's day in 2007, when Aron had called up this young lady to offer her the job at the firm. The moment the words had left his mouth, he had heard a loud and distinct thumping, repeated and rhythmic. Aron had turned to look at Sheela, puzzled, and Sheela had shrugged. A few moments later, the thumping had stopped and Pamela Genise's voice had come down the line—formal, polite and a tad (just a tad) out of breath. 'Thanks very much, Mr Finkelstein. I'm happy to accept.' Months later, when Pam had well and proper settled at the firm, she had confessed over lunch one day that as soon as Aron had offered her the job, she had got out of her chair and jumped for joy. Sheela and Aron had burst out laughing because, for them, at last, the mystery had been solved!

Now Sheela looked at Pam and suddenly knew that she couldn't let this talented, committed, warm-hearted attorney leave so easily. 'MurthyWest,' Sheela had said suddenly, without thinking.

'What?' Pamela had asked, her head jerking up.

'This firm needs a presence on the west coast. In Seattle, close to your parents. MurthyWest, we'll call it. You will open the office for us, and you will be in charge of it.'

33

Señór Javier Ramirez, a native of Honduras, had come to the United States on an L-1 visa, a non-immigrant work visa that had a relatively short-term validity. He was an employee of a manufacturing company, whose headquarters were in the United States and had a presence in Honduras. On one of his work trips to the unit in Tegucigalpa, the capital city of Honduras, he had taken his wife Isabella and their little daughter Camila along with him, so they could visit family.

As Ramirez's dependents, Isabella and Camila were in the United States on an L-2 visa. This meant that Isabella could work on an L-2 EAD, an Employment Authorization Document, and had got herself a job as a software developer. Her employers appreciated her very much because she was excellent at her work, and they also appreciated the fact that they did not have to sponsor her papers. When the time came for her to take a short holiday, her company had been happy to give her a few days off from work to visit her family in Honduras.

After a pleasant stay in Tegucigalpa, just two days before they were scheduled to fly back to their lives and jobs in America, Señór Ramirez had informed Isabella that he would not be allowing her to accompany him to the United States. There had been no love lost between the couple, and for some years now, almost since Camila had been born, they had stayed together more for the child's sake and the convenience of having a partner around than because of any deep attachment between them. But they had always been polite to each other and refrained from quarreling in front of the child. For the most part, their earlier interactions and exchanges had lapsed into silence. Nevertheless, this sudden turn of events hit Isabella like a bolt from the blue! Without a word, she had retreated into the room with Camila, locked the door and gone through their documents. Everything was gone. Clearly, Javier had removed them. That was probably what he had been doing when he had opted to stay home from church the previous day.

Camila was sent outside to play with her cousins while her parents discussed the matter. Javier informed Isabella that he wanted a divorce in exchange for returning her papers to her. For all the quietness of his manner, he had nevertheless been adamant, and no amount of reasoning had helped to change his mind. In a panic, Isabella had called Murthy Law Firm that very same day, and got in touch with Anna Stepanova.

Anna had gone over the case painstakingly with her, trying to look at it from every angle. But the situation appeared fairly straightforward. Isabella and Camila needed their passports with those L-2 visas stamped into them, or else there was no way they would be able to re-enter the United States.

When she had regretfully told Isabella as much, Isabella had been distraught.

'Senóra Ramirez,' Anna had said, 'I am more sorry than I can convey, that we will be unable to help you. The only advice I can give you is that no matter what you do, do not agree to give your husband a divorce. Once you divorce him, even if he returns your passport to you, that L-2 stamp will no longer be valid. Your daughter Camila's will be, but you will no longer be considered your husband's dependent, and your L-2 visa will be null and void. You will lose all hope of returning to the US right away, unless you apply for a job afresh and start all over. And frankly, Senōra, given the immigration policies under this government, there is no telling how that will turn out for you.'

'I understand, Ms Stepanova. Thank you very much for your time.' Isabella had been weeping as she said those words.

'I hope you know,' Anna added, 'that there will be no legal fee for this consultation.'

The weekly attorney meeting was held, as usual, at 1 p.m. the next day, which was a Tuesday. Anna brought up the Ramirez case, and went over it in detail for her colleagues. As she spoke, she saw Sheela sit forward and listen intently. She frowned a few times.

'I'd like to speak with this woman, Anna. If the husband can be convinced to get on a conference call with me and Camila—'

'Isabella,' Anna corrected.

'That's right, Isabella. Camila is the daughter, is she?' Anna nodded and Sheela went on, 'If Isabella can convince her husband to come to the phone, I will speak to the two of them together on a conference call. Can you try and arrange that, Anna?'

'Yes, of course.'

* * *

It had taken Isabella three days to convince Javier to at least speak with the immigration lawyer for a few minutes. He was due to fly back to the United States the next morning—without Isabella and Camila, as his wife had flatly refused to let the child leave without her—and Isabella had almost given up hope, when he had suddenly relented and agreed to a telephone conversation. Perhaps it was not her pleading as much as it was the fact that his daughter no longer looked at him that may have done the trick.

Sheela had had a quick chat with Isabella two days prior. It had been done confidentially, when Javier was not at home.

'If you give him the divorce, your L-2 becomes null and void anyway, so it won't matter even if he returns the passport to you,' Sheela had said, repeating what Anna had advised her because she understood that relationships between husband and wife could be very complex, and often advice didn't always work the first time. They tended to be more attached, to get under each other's skins more thoroughly than people in other relationships. She was not sure that Javier would not succeed in bringing his wife around to giving him that divorce, if he persisted long enough. It turned out Sheela was right. In the last few days, Isabella had been worn thin by her husband's incessant badgering.

'And do not let him take Camila with him,' added Sheela quickly.

'He proposed just that! He proposed that I should let him take Camila with him back to the United States. He keeps saying how much she loves her school and her friends, how lost she will be without them. And she is, Ms Murthy! She is heartbroken at not being able to go back. That is the only home she has ever known. Honduras is a strange place to her. Javier says that I should not force Camila to remain in Honduras just because I am not willing to let her go without me. He says that he will take her to America now, and as soon as I give him the divorce, he will help me look for a job at a company that will sponsor my H-1B. Maybe he is right...'

'Maybe. Or, there is the possibility that you may never see your daughter or the United States again. Please Isabella, I know what I am talking about. Please give me a chance to speak with him, negotiate with him. If you can manage to get him on a phone with me, I will do whatever I can to help all three of you,' said Sheela.

The call happened two nights later. After dealing with the Ravi Kumar case, Sheela read the Ramirez file and then got on the call soon after. Over 3,000 miles away in Teguchigalpa, both husband and wife were on the other line.

'Thank you very much for agreeing to speak with me, Mr Ramirez,' said Sheela politely.

Expecting hostility from this lady lawyer his wife had dug up behind his back, Javier Ramirez was taken aback by the pleasant, neutral tone of her voice. So, that's how it was going to be, was it? Fine. He managed a non-committal grunt because he wasn't about to get coerced into taking Isabella back with him to America, certainly not by a sweet-talking lawyer!

'Isabella tells me that you wish to take Camila back to the US but you would rather Isabella stay on in Honduras. From what I am given to understand, your wife and you have been leading separate lives under the same roof for many years now. It seemed like a comfortable arrangement. May I ask you what has changed?'

A sudden flare of hostility caused him to say, 'You are going to represent my wife. You are on her side. Why should I talk to you or explain my reasons to you?'

'My colleague has already told your wife quite clearly that we will not represent her because this is a case we will not be able to win,' replied Sheela calmly. 'I am not representing anybody today. I am speaking on behalf of all three of you, Mr Ramirez, the whole family. I am speaking on behalf of Camila, who is a little child and does not deserve to watch her parents tear each other apart.'

Javier was silent.

'*Por favor*, Javier. *Por favor escucha lo que quiere decirte!*' pleaded Isabella fervently.

Taking this to be her cue to continue, Sheela said, 'You will lose your child if you pursue this track, Mr Ramirez—'

'I will fight for custody!' he snarled.

'By all means, do so. You might even win, which means Camila will have to live with you for the next eight years. But after that, what? Do you think she will not remember that you abandoned her mother and took her away from the woman who gave birth to her?'

He was silent.

'Why do you want this divorce, Mr Ramirez?' asked Sheela, suddenly getting the sense that there was more to this matter than met the eye.

Silence.

'Is there someone else? Have you met someone else?'

Silence.

But Isabella on the other line saw the look on her husband's face and asked anxiously, '*¿Quién es ella*, Javier?'

He said nothing.

'Is it someone at work?' probed Sheela gently.

'*Sí*,' he said, at last. Yes.

Isabella broke down at his answer, and Sheela felt that it was better to take charge of the situation.

'Mr Ramirez, if you want to marry this other woman then I understand your reasons for asking Isabella for a divorce.'

'Why is *she* crying?' asked Javier resentfully. 'It is not as if she loves me. She has never loved me!'

'Let Isabella and Camila come back into the country,' interposed Sheela. 'Give Isabella the chance to approach her employer to sponsor her H-1B. As soon as they agree, you both can file for a divorce. It will only be another six months or so that you will be able to tie up all the loose ends. In the meantime, come to some understanding on how you would like to share Camila. Do it in a way that will give her the chance to enjoy the love of both her parents. She shouldn't have to choose, Mr Ramirez. No child should have to choose between her parents. Won't your girlfriend wait for you for a few months to leave this marriage in a decent and honorable way? Would she want you to cheat a woman out of her legal rights in order to marry her?' questioned Sheela.

Javier was silent for a long time. Then slowly he admitted, 'She will not want it. She has told me many, many times. She is a good woman and she understands these things. She will wait for me for as long as it takes,' he replied. 'It is I who am impatient to get on with my life.' The softening in his tone when he mentioned this other woman made Sheela's heart go out to him. Perhaps he would find his chance at happiness after all, poor man.

'Then you will let Isabella and Camila accompany you back to the Unites States tomorrow?'

'*Sí*,' he said in a low voice. 'I will.'

As the couple rang off, Isabella cried, '*Gracias por todos*, Ms Murthy! Thank you for what you have done for me and for Camila. *Nunca lo olvidaré! Gracias!*' Javier only murmured, almost under his breath, 'God bless you…' But somehow it meant more to Sheela than if he had thanked her as profusely as Isabella had done.

* * *

Vasant needed a few shirts, and Sheela wanted to buy some things to take back home to India on their upcoming trip. She needed some clothes for herself too, but found herself thinking of the cheapest stores in the mall instead of the more expensive ones. Still, even after all these years and all the money she had earned and given away to the needy, when it came to herself she only gravitated to the least expensive stores. Perhaps it stemmed from the early years of not having much, when Indu had scrimped and saved to get new clothes for her children and to bring food to the table.

As they walked around the mall, Vasant wandered off to make his purchases, while Sheela hesitated, trying to decide which shop she would enter first. That's when she saw a familiar-looking Indian gentleman in his mid-thirties, accompanied by a beautiful woman and two children, heading in her direction. Sheela stopped and frowned, for she simply could not place the man, even though she was certain they had met before. The other three were not familiar at all. At that moment, the man looked up from his phone and saw Sheela. His face broke into a smile of genuine gladness, and he hurried ahead of the others.

'Ms Murthy!' he exclaimed, taking both her hands in his own and beaming down at her with so much pleasure that she couldn't help smiling tentatively back at him.

'You don't remember me, do you?' he asked, laughing.

And then it came back to her. 'Sharat! Of course, it's Sharat Joshi, isn't it?'

'That's right!' Now the other three had caught up with them, and Sheela smiled past Sharat's shoulder and held out her hand to his wife.

'And you must be Priya.'

The lady's smile faltered a little just when Sharat said, smoothly, 'Aparna. this is my wife, Aparna. And those are our children, Rhea and Om.'

Sheela was quite taken aback, so much so, that all she could do was continue speaking as if nothing had happened. The children greeted her politely and then went off in the direction of a Gap outlet at the end of the row of stores.

'Aparna, *tu zha*. You go ahead with the kids, *mi laukar yete*,' he told his wife in their native tongue. Saying her goodbyes, Aparna hurried after her children, while Sharat remained behind to speak with Sheela.

'What happened, Sharat?' she asked him, when Aparna was out of earshot.

'Priya left me,' he replied simply. 'It turned out that she was unable to forgive me for not bringing her to this country sooner. We broke up two years after she moved here.' There was no bitterness in his voice; it was as if he was speaking about someone else's life.

'So it was all for nothing then,' said Sheela sadly. 'All that effort we took—'

'But it wasn't!' he protested, taking her hand. 'How can you say that? You restored my honor among my people back home! You restored my faith in myself as a husband because I didn't just marry a woman and leave her in the lurch, but was able to bring her to come and live with me like I had promised her I would. I was able to do what I had to do, and when it didn't work out, I was able to move on with a clear conscience. Only because of you!'

His eyes wandered to his wife standing some distance away at the entrance of the Gap store. His expression softened as he said, 'Aparna is a lovely person. We're very happy together, Ms Murthy.'

Sheela was thrilled to hear him say this. Suddenly she asked, 'And your mother? Does she get along with Aparna?'

'Of course, she doesn't!' exclaimed Sharat with a naughty smile. 'What kind of a mother-in-law would it make her if she did?'

34

Shahid Ahmed Raza headed the technical department of a large, multi-national firm in Baltimore. An old client of Sheela's, it was through him that she met Ghulam *Bhai*, Shahid's older brother. His much older brother. In fact, as the two men took their seats across the table from her, Sheela's first thought was that they could have been father and son. Her second was that Ghulam *Bhai* reminded her of Bilawal Khan, the kindly and much-loved playmate of her childhood years in Udhampur back in India. Bilawal *bhaiya* must now be approximately the same age as the gentleman sitting opposite her, and Sheela prayed, for a fleeting moment, that Noora had grown up well and was taking good care of her father. Then, Shahid began to speak, and Sheela brought her attention back to him.

'My brother and his family would like to migrate to America, Sheela. Now that I am a citizen, I would like them to join me in this country and start a new life here.'

'Very well,' said Sheela. 'What is it that you do in India, Ghulam *Bhai*?' she asked, switching to Hindi.

'I own a small mechanic garage in Lucknow, madam,' he replied.

'So you are the proprietor of the garage as well as a trained mechanic?'

'*Haan ji*, I am both. I started off working at my uncle's garage when I was nine years old. I don't have a college degree or anything.

213

Everything that I know I learnt under the bonnet of a car, just by working with my hands,' said the elderly gentleman. He was soft-spoken and polite. The Urdu term for it was *tehzeeb*, which implied propriety and decency of a deeper sort, when conducting oneself in all matters. Sheela recalled the word, and felt that it applied well to this man.

She also realized that without a degree, he did not have the requisite technical qualifications to be able to be sponsored by a US employer for an H-1B or an L-1. She told the brothers as much, adding, 'Your only option is to apply for the FB-4, to be filed by Shahid.'

'The FB-4, madam?'

'Sorry, I should have been more clear. I meant the Family Based Fourth Preference Category, meant for the siblings of US citizens. Shahid, as your brother, will have to sponsor you and your family.'

'I will, Sheela. Gladly,' said Shahid.

'Then, we should move quickly. Trump is planning to eliminate the chain family migration. The earlier we file the better because we don't know how long that will hold good, before the option is axed.'

'How long will the process take?' asked Shahid.

'Between ten and fifteen years.'

A worried frown creased Shahid's brow. 'What if it is eliminated after we file the papers but before the green cards come through?' he questioned.

'Generally, laws are prospective, not retroactive. If a law is passed effective today, the government tends to not go back to cases that were filed in the past, where they have cashed the check and permitted people to make their future plans based on the petition filed,' explained Sheela.

'Okay, but worst case scenario, what if they do?'

'In that case we'll have to consider our legal options, including challenging the United States Government. We'll sue. They can't take someone's money and then turn them away.'

'You know, Sheela, my brother would come to this country and work as hard as he has worked back home in Lucknow. I will open a garage for him here. There is no vehicle yet invented that my brother can't repair!' cried Shahid with unmistakable pride, and Sheela smiled.

'*Arrey, bus karo,*' reprimanded the older brother gently. 'Do not boast like that.'

'But it is true!' insisted Shahid, over his brother's protests. 'We lost our parents when I was very young, and *Bhaijaan* has been both father and mother to me. He worked to put me through school and college, until I got a scholarship and came to the United States. Growing up, we managed on very little because we were a large family. And yet, even after I began to earn well in the US and wanted to send money home, *Bhaijaan* would not allow it.'

'There was no need,' said the older brother. 'Both your sisters-in-law are good women and their wants were few. They raised the children to be undemanding as well,' said Ghulam *Bhai*.

'How many children do you have, Ghulam *Bhai*?' asked Sheela.

'Four, madam.'

'And who is the second sister-in-law you speak of?' asked Sheela, thinking that there must be a third brother who had not yet been mentioned.

'My second wife, Ambreen. I have two children from Salma, and two from Ambreen.'

Sheela's mind froze momentarily at this bit of information, and then went into a spin. For once in her life, she found herself completely at a loss for words.

'What is it?' asked the elderly gentlemen in concern, seeing the dismay on her face.

'Ghulam *Bhai*,' she said, after a small pause. 'Ghulam *Bhai*, I am so sorry to tell you this but United States law doesn't recognize a second marriage. Only the first one is considered legal. This country will consider a petition for you and your first wife, but not your second one.'

Shahid's face fell, but Ghulam *Bhai* remained stoic.

'I see,' was all he said.

However, Shahid asked anxiously, 'Is there no other way, Sheela?'

Sheela was thoughtful, turning all the possible options and legal solutions to this problem over in her mind before she responded. There was, indeed, an option. But she was almost certain that it wouldn't work under those circumstances. If the husband himself didn't have an educational degree or a qualification…

Nevertheless, Sheela ventured, 'If Ambreen, in her own capacity, can get a job in the US, where her employer agrees to file for her H-1B—'

Shahid who had sat forward eagerly when Sheela started to speak now slumped back in his chair.

'My second sister-in-law is not educated, Sheela. Neither is the first one, for that matter. They both married young, and at a time when female education in our community was not commonplace. We're talking about forty, even forty-five years ago.'

'Yes, I know,' said Sheela, who had expected an answer like this in the first place.

'Is there another solution, then?' asked Shahid.

Sheela glanced at Ghulam *bhai*. He was listening keenly to her but his face betrayed neither hope, longing nor despair. She hesitated for a moment and suddenly he smiled and nodded, as if to encourage her to speak freely.

'Er … you will have to divorce one of your wives and bring the other one, the legal one, with you to the US.'

Shahid dropped his eyes but Ghulam *Bhai* continued to meet Sheela's gaze with his straightforward one.

'That will not be possible, madam. You see, I have a duty towards each of them and to the children from both. When I married these women, I made them each a promise, to look after and protect them. I can never break that promise. Neither my honor nor my religion will permit me to do so.' After a tiny pause, he added softly, 'They are both very dear to me, madam.'

Sheela suddenly felt bad for suggesting what she did. 'I'm sorry, Ghulam *Bhai*,' she said contritely. 'I shouldn't have—'

'You are a good lawyer. You were only doing your job, and I appreciate your giving me all the options. So there is nothing to be sorry for, no. America is not the place for me after all, I suppose.'

'But *Bhaijaan*—' protested Shahid.

'No Shahid. You have done your best but Allah doesn't want it to be so. I was happy with my life in India. Now I will return home to my family and to my garage, and continue to be happy. I have no regrets at all.'

35

In October 2018, Sheela and Vasant traveled to India as usual, on their bi-annual trip. Since the passing of Radha Bai and Shankar Nayak, Vasant had reduced the frequency of his visits from once every few months, to twice in a year. For Sheela too, coming home to Bangalore had lost much of its charm without Daddy being there. Indu was busy with frequent yoga camps and the free homeopathic clinic she ran. Shree continued to live at home with her mother, even after her daughter moved to Delhi to study law. Now one of the better-known obstetricians of the city, Shree was liked by her patients for her kind and skillful approach to their medical problems. She had converted a part of the compound area of the Indiranagar bungalow into a practice of her own. This, along with the stray dog shelter she ran, kept her busy, too busy in fact, to spend much time with Sheela when she visited.

Suman, now an ophthalmologist, was married and settled in Mumbai with her husband and daughter. She had made quite a success of the eye hospital she had started, and counted among her patients many Bollywood film stars! Reluctant to leave her patients and her family, she nevertheless tried to take a few days off from work and fly down to Bangalore whenever Sheela was in town. Those few days with her younger sister gave Sheela much happiness. Whenever

Indu came upstairs to Sheela's part of the house with jaggery *payasa*, lemon rice and other delicacies that she had prepared especially for her, Sheela observed how much her mother had changed over the years. Indu had grown gentler and less guarded in her demonstration of her affection for her daughters and her pride in their achievements. She no longer kept her feelings locked away behind a grim exterior, as she had in the old days.

Murthy Immigration Services Private Limited, in Chennai, was situated across the street from where Vasant's sister, Sheila, lived. Senthil efficiently managed that office, and the firm's client base had slowly increased over the years. Sheela and Vasant made it a point to travel to Chennai almost every time they visited India, in order to spend a few days at the liason office, going over things with Senthil. Sheela would also meet with consular officers at the US Consulate in Chennai. Every time the post of the Non-immigrant Visa (NIV) Chief passed into new hands at the Consulate in Chennai (initially, the only consular post in South India), Sheela unfailingly made an appointment and went across to spend a few minutes with them. She felt this to be her duty, being an officer of the American courts. Moreover, most of her clients from India were assigned their visa interviews at Chennai, and she made it a point to thank the NIV Chief and the other consular officers in person, knowing that it was their decision, and sometimes at their discretion, that her clients had been granted passage into the United States. Over the years, the officers too had come to trust this competent, intelligent attorney, who always spoke with candor and never misrepresented facts in order to coax or mislead them into granting her clients the visa.

Sheela also tried to visit the US Consulates in Hyderabad and Mumbai whenever possible. The consular post at Hyderabad came into existence much later due to the heavy demand from the then State of Andhra Pradesh (now in Telangana State). She had an overwhelming number of clients from the Hyderabad region, where she was popularly known as Murthy *garu*, *garu* being the honorific commonly used in the local language.

Interestingly, a case had come up for Sheela's intervention a few months prior. A man from Arcot district in Tamil Nadu had entered the United States on an H-1B visa and was having difficulty procuring the H-4 for his new bride to join him in Cincinnati, where he lived and worked. The consulate in Chennai had denied her the H-4 on the grounds that the marriage was one of convenience and hence was not valid. The reason they cited for this was that, while the wedding invitation card, the marriage certificate, the witness signatures and the wedding photographs had all undoubtedly been submitted to the consulate in Chennai along with the application for the H-4 visa, the officiating priest at the ceremony had been missing from the wedding photographs!

At his wits' end, the young bridegroom had approached Sheela, who made a phone call from her Baltimore office to the Consular Officer in Chennai. She had patiently conveyed to him that in the particular community to which the bride and groom belonged, having the officiating priest in the wedding photos was considered ill luck, and was hence a strict no-no. A certain sect of Tamilians adhered strongly to this belief, and was unpersuadable on the matter.

The consular officer, being familiar with Sheela and her reputation for honesty, had immediately taken her word for it and issued the H-4 visa, as Sheela had known he would. But it was precisely because of her confidence in her ability to convince the consular officer that Sheela had felt compelled to first verify the truth of the bridegroom's explanation for the missing priest. Instead of simply picking up the phone and calling the consulate in Chennai, Sheela had asked the client for a few days to get to the bottom of the matter. After the client's departure, she had telephoned Senthil in Chennai. Giving him the name of the particular community, she had asked him to delve into the matter. Only a couple of days later, when Senthil had called back to say that the bridegroom's claim was true had Sheela made that call to the consular officer. To her way of thinking, the higher the trust people placed in her, the greater was her responsibility to be deserving of it.

* * *

Quite recently, during lunch hour at work, the team of attorneys at Murthy Law Firm had been seated around the table enjoying the few minutes of rest from their busy schedules. Lunch had been a grand affair that day. It was the Indian food day, and Sheela's passion for feeding people ensured that the best Indian restaurant in town had catered the meal. Halfway through eating a piece of butter chicken, Joel Yanovich had looked up from showing Anna and Sheela the latest pictures of little Sagan, and exclaimed to the room in general, 'I almost forgot to mention an article I read yesterday.'

Did you know that in India, in fact right there in Hyderabad where MLF has a liason office, there is a temple called the Visa Temple? People go there to pray to god to grant them their visas.'

'Which god?' asked Anna.

'I don't know how to pronounce his name. Baa-laa-zhi, or something like that?' He glanced at Sheela for confirmation.

'Balaji,' said Sheela, correcting his pronunciation.

'A temple for visas?' asked Khorzad interestedly. While Khorzad was Indian himself, the temple that Joel was referring to was a Hindu one, and Khorzad belonged to a different religion— Zoroastrianism. The religion had originated in Persia, or modern-day Iran, and had later spread to Gujarat on the west coast of India. The Zoroastrians were also known as Parsis or Parsees, and were fire-worshippers. Consequently, they did not subscribe to the vast pantheon of Hindu gods and goddesses. The one thing that the two religions had in common, however, was their belief in the ultimate sanctity of fire.

'It's true,' said Joel. 'The devotees carry their passports with them into the temple. They take it in turns to hand the passports over to the priest, who lays them on the altar at the feet of the deity for a bit and then returns them all blessed and sanctified. Then the visa aspirants walk around the sanctum eight times and leave for their visa interviews. When the visas get approved—apparently almost everybody who prays there gets an approval—they return to circumambulate the sanctum a further 108 times to give thanks.'

The others listened carefully, amazed at an idea so novel. Then Joel said, 'Sheela, here's what we should do. We should hire a billboard outside this visa temple and advertise ourselves with a slogan that reads something like, "Murthy Law Firm: Your Prayers Have Been Answered!" That way people will get to know about us.'

Now, on her most recent trip to India, Sheela spent a few hours at the Hyderabad liaison office, which she had not had the time to do on her previous visit. Finding everything to be in good order, she had proceeded for her meeting with the officer at the American Consulate in Hyderabad. After that, with considerable time to spare before her flight back to Chennai, where she would join Vasant and Senthil, she was suddenly overcome by a curiosity that Joel had piqued with his story over lunch back in the US office. A visa temple!

It didn't take long to find out because everybody outside the Consulate, from the applicants to the security guards, knew exactly where the Chilkur Balaji temple was situated. Sheela got into the hired car and requested to be driven there.

Belying its popularity and the massive footfalls it received, the temple structure itself was not a large one. Its entrance called to mind a pretty, brightly-painted doll house while inside, everything was for real. The priest was meticulous in his worship, the devotees utterly invested in the belief of the sure success of prayers offered here. Everything was just as Joel had described it. Sheela wandered around quietly by herself, watching the way the devotees sandwiched their passports between folded palms and raised them high above their heads as they circumambulated the sanctum sanctorum.

Suddenly, there was a stir among the crowds, and people began to turn their heads and whisper animatedly to each other. Soon others started to turn and point as well. Sheela wondered what was going on, when she realized that they were pointing at *her*!

'That is Murthy *garu*! *Choodundi*, Murthy *garu* had come here! Murthy *garu ikkada vachchinaru*!' people cried in a chorus and rushed over to Sheela, producing bits of paper and pens that they were carrying on their persons. They wanted her autograph! But how did they—?

'You are very famous here, Murthy *garu*,' explained one young lady who later confided that she had applied to do a master's program in US and was only awaiting her visa interview. 'Many people have taken the help of Murthy Law Firm to go to America. Everybody knows about you; your face is all over the Internet!' she beamed. 'That is how we all know you!'

Far away in Baltimore, Joel was asleep with Stephanie by his side. It was midnight when a discreet beep woke him. Sleepily, he reached for his phone, and Stephanie stirred. Joel kept still until she fell back to sleep, and then he looked at his phone again. There was a WhatsApp message from Sheela, with a photograph of some kind. It was a photo of Sheela standing there with her customary bright smile, surrounded by people. Lots and lots of people, all doing their best to squeeze into the frame and be photographed with her. Sheela had accompanied the attachment with a caption that read: 'They all know us here. Your Prayers have been Answered!'

* * *

Vasant and Sheela were due to leave for Bangalore around midday, and then for Baltimore two days later. That morning, Sheela and Senthil arrived at the Murthy Immigration Services office in Alwarpet, Chennai, around 9 a.m., hoping to wrap up some final, case-related work before it would be time to depart for the airport. When Senthil's SUV pulled up outside the office, they saw a young man waiting at the front step of the one-story house that had been converted into the law office space. Beside him was a tiny overnight bag.

The security guard approached Senthil's window and informed him in Tamil that the gentleman had arrived by the 5.30 a.m. bus from Tirupati, and had come straight to the Murthy Immigration Services office. He had been waiting there ever since, in the hope of meeting Sheela.

Unbidden, and entirely unexpected, came the memory of Shankar Nayak who, so many years ago, had come to Bangalore with a similar overnight bag, looking for her. Sheela was suddenly overwhelmed with emotion and had to blink back her tears for her father-in-law. Her brisk, no-nonsense, mighty-hearted father-in-law had been very special to her, and she still missed him. But what would he say to her now if he saw her sitting in the car letting emotion overwhelm her when another human being waited outside in the hot sun for her to help him? This brought her back to her senses very quickly.

'Perhaps you should have taken him inside and fetched him something to eat, Venkatesan,' she suggested to the security guard. 'He could have freshened up and waited inside for us, poor man!'

'Madam, I asked him over and over again but he refused. He said he didn't want to cause any bother, he only wanted your help,' Venkatesan mumbled contritely.

The young man on the front step got to his feet the moment he saw Sheela approach him, and folded his hands in greeting. 'Forgive me for coming like this, ma'am. When I heard you were in town, I just *had* to seize this opportunity to meet you!'

Sheela turned at the sound of the car and saw that Senthil, instead of parking, was driving away again. She looked inquiringly at Venkatesan, who said, 'Sir asked me to tell you the he is going to pack some breakfast for this gentleman.' Sheela nodded. But she felt lucky to have Senthil, with his thoughtful ways and instinctive kindness, as part of her team. She took the client inside and seated him in her office with a cup of hot, sweetened tea.

'I am Rajeev Naidu, ma'am,' he said, and Sheela picked up her ears, for both the name and voice were familiar, although the face wasn't.

'I spoke to you over a year ago in your US office … not in person, ma'am!' he corrected quickly when he saw her puzzled frown. 'It was not in person. I was in India. We had a phone conversation, you in Baltimore, me in India and my wife Veena in Philadelphia.'

Suddenly, Sheela recollected the case! Yes, she had 'met' with the couple over the phone in order to understand the details of the case before handing it over to one of the other attorneys to work on.

'But that was a year ago, Rajeev. What is the situation now?'

'It is as it was then, ma'am. I am still here, and Veena and the children are still in Philly.'

Sheela stared at him, aghast! A year since he had been separated from his family. One whole year! And she and her firm had not been able to help him! She felt shame wash over her that a person in her care had suffered this way. What would Papa, her father-in-law, say to her if he were here now? What would Daddy say? For the very first time, Sheela was glad that both fathers were no longer here to witness how she had failed in her duty!

Senthil entered with a parcel in his hand, and Sheela quickly fetched a plate and cutlery for the *idli*, *sambar* and chutney that Senthil had brought for Rajeev's breakfast. After a quick visit to the office restroom, where Rajeev washed the dust from the journey off his face and hands, he sat at the table and ate gratefully, hungrily, until the food was all gone. In the meantime, Sheela and Senthil took care of the business that they had originally come to sort out that day.

Once Rajeev was ready, he took a chair before Sheela and she said, 'Rajeev, I am afraid I do not recall the details of your case. But if you could tell them to me once again, this time I will do everything in my power to get you back into the United States!'

Comforted by the kindness of her manner, Rajeev told her his story, which went like this: 'Both Veena and I have jobs in the US. We are both on H-1Bs, neither of us is on a dependent on the other. We've lived in Philly for many years now, and our two children were born there; they are American citizens. My H-1B visa had expired but I had continued working legally in US, pursuant to an H-1B extension that had been approved by the USCIS. When my grandmother got sick two years ago, I packed for a three-week trip and rushed back to India. She lived in Tirupati with my parents—that is our hometown, ma'am—and I got to spend the last few days of her life with her. I was lucky to be with her when she passed away,' said Rajeev quietly, and Sheela smiled. Vasant had done the same for his mother, and had later told her how much it meant to him to have been able to do that.

'After the funeral, I applied for a new visa stamp—a visa folio they call it, I think ma'am?' and Sheela nodded. 'I applied for the visa folio from the American Consulate, so I could re-enter the United States once the death ceremonies for my grandmother were over. But the consulate refused. It has been nearly two years and they still have not issued the stamp.'

'On what grounds?' asked Sheela.

'They seem to be looking for a reason to deny me. That's all I can say. Because they dug up information on me and discovered that the work experience I had put on my application the first time I applied for the US visa so many years ago was not strictly correct.'

'What do you mean?'

'I mean that one of the companies I claimed to have worked for did not exist.' He looked a little shame-faced and dropped his eyes.

But then he looked up again and said, 'I needed the job in America, I needed the visa. I did not lie about my education. The other two were legitimate places I had worked at. I was ashamed of doing it at that time but I no longer am, Ms Murthy. I was young then, desperate. Since then, I have held two jobs in the US and worked hard and steadily for my employers on both occasions. I have been promoted time and again, received raises and bonuses … I am no longer ashamed.' Sheela nodded in understanding.

'The fact is,' she interposed, 'that under the law, work experience is not a requirement for obtaining the H-1B petition approval or the H-1B visa.'

'Still, they accused me of misrepresenting facts in order to pad up my resumé, and insisted that the reason I had got that first job in the US was because of this false claim, and that I had very likely deprived a legitimate US worker of the opportunity to get that same job. They stamped into my passport a notation with a 212(a)(6)(C).'

Sheela sat forward in concern. 'That is tantamount to fraud!' she hissed. 'They stamped that in your passport?'

'Yes,' he replied, holding out the passport to her, open at the page that bore the stamp. Sheela glanced down at it.

'What does this mean, ma'am?'

'It means,' said Sheela grimly, 'a potential lifetime ban on ever entering the United States, either on a non-immigrant or even an immigrant visa.'

Rajeev stared at her, speechless. But Sheela only looked back at him, anger and frustration flashing in her eyes as she added, 'It is the times we live in, Rajeev. It is the stand *this* government has chosen to take on immigration in a country that is made up of immigrants. Don't blame the consular officer. He is only doing what he has been instructed to do.'

There was only one way around this ban on Rajeev's re-entering the United States now—a Non-immigrant Visa Waiver. But that meant a steep uphill task. It usually required a minimum of a five-year wait, and a showing of extreme hardship and other extenuating circumstances as reasons for why the consular officer should recommend a waiver to the Administrative Review Office (ARO) in the US. And if that was difficult, then obtaining the Immigrant Visa Waiver was even tougher. Because, in order to do so, one would have to demonstrate extreme hardship to a US Citizen or Permanent Resident family member!

In Rajeev Naidu's case, the visa process had taken so long that in the meantime his wife, Veena, had become a Permanent Resident. The kids had been US citizens by birth, and so the person who was fighting Rajeev's case—in this instance Sheela—would have to establish the suffering of the family as a whole.

* * *

Six days after her meeting with Rajeev Naidu in Chennai, having since returned to the US, Sheela found herself in the waiting room of the child therapist's office in downtown Philadelphia. She flipped through a magazine, and just when she came upon an article she found interesting, the receptionist told her that the therapist was ready to see her.

'I'm sorry to take up so much of your time when you have patients waiting outside to consult you,' apologized Sheela. But the therapist waved aside her apologies and replied, 'I am happy to do this, Ms Murthy. I have been very worried about Aryan myself. I'm afraid that he's not doing so well.'

They discussed the case briefly. Veena had given her consent for the therapist to share those bits of information with Sheela that pertained to the boy's current emotional state, in the hope that it would help her build a case with the American consular officer to allow the child's father back into the country. As they spoke, Sheela began to form a mental picture of how things were at the Naidu residence. Veena had already told her much of it over the phone. But this time it was not a distressed, disembodied voice reaching her down a telephone line. It was pictures made by a six-year-old child who had lost his father and did not know where to find him.

* * *

Sheela Murthy submitted a carefully compiled file of evidence that she and her team of attorneys and paralegals at MLF had put together. The contents of this file demonstrated the trauma and hardships that the family of Rajeev Naidu had undergone in the years that he had been unable to return home to them. One document was an affidavit from a neighbor, a friend of the family, detailing the hardships she had witnessed the Naidus go through. The affidavit also mentioned the trauma that one of the children was suffering and that too was observed by this neighbor.

The second document was an affidavit from Veena Naidu, listing the struggles she was undergoing as a single parent. The consequences of being the sole breadwinner of the family as Rajeev's employers had long since terminated his employment, paying off the mortgage that had originally been designed for a two-income family, juggling the children's busy schedules with the demands of her own job, and her inability to afford day care or even a baby sitter now that the household income had been cut in half. In addition to this, she was also faced with the challenge of looking out for ways that would help her distraught children cope with the loss of the daily presence of their father, whom they had not seen in two years.

The third document was a signed report from their child's therapist that outlined the mental condition of Veena and Rajeev's six-year-old son. The child was facing bullying in school, had grown withdrawn and had developed stress-induced diseases like asthma. He was being told by other children that he was the son of an 'illegal immigrant', and was often asked when he was going to be 'deported back to his own country'.

But the document that changed the mind of the US consular officer in the end was not even an official one. It was just a little drawing, scribbled in color pencil that the six-year-old had made one day during a therapy session. His therapist had thought to include it in her report at the last minute. Now, this drawing fell out from among the papers, and the consular officer picked it off the floor and gazed down at it. On it was a little boy wearing a green shirt and blue shorts, curled up on the floor with his knees drawn tightly to his chest, his arms wrapped around his stomach. All around him were fingers—roughly drawn, fat, stubby, disembodied fingers—that pointed directly at him. In the distance was a man who stood watching silently. The officer could not understand whether the child thought the man was staying away out of choice or out of helplessness. But *he*, the officer, knew the answer. And he thought to himself, 'It is time to correct the situation. It is time to let this man return home.'

36

The girls swarmed all over Macy's, looking at the perfumes and cosmetics, taking clothes off the racks and holding them up against themselves before casting them aside to try on different ones. Sheela stood back and watched quietly, enjoying their enthusiasm and delight; being here was a novel experience for them.

Only Shirley hung back, looking around herself with vague, absent eyes.

Sheela could not understand this girl. In the time that she had been working as a volunteer with the Girl Scouts of Central Maryland, an organization of which these fifteen young girls were members, she had never once seen Shirley smile or look happy. She hadn't made friends with the others, never shared confidences with them, discussed boys she had crushes on or giggled over silly things that happened at school. It worried Sheela that a fourteen-year-old girl should have such little sense of joy in her life that even an accidental, fleeting smile should fail to pass her lips.

All fifteen girls who had accompanied Sheela that day were teenage daughters of incarcerated mothers. Begun in 1992, the program was the brain-child of a Maryland district court judge. It was developed with the help of the National Institute of Justice and the Maryland Correctional Institution for Women, where more than two-thirds of the inmates are mothers. Sheela actively helped expand and promote the program.

With their mothers in prison for various offenses—mostly drug abuse and peddling—a few of the girls lived in foster homes, and the others with their grandmothers, who had stepped in to protect them from having to live with strangers until their mothers did or did not return to make decent homes for them. In every one of the cases, the fathers had left. Except for Judith and Simone in the group, none of the others could even recollect what their fathers looked like.

Shirley lived with her sixty-six-year-old grandmother, Rayhelle, who worked at a grocery store to be able to afford to keep her granddaughter with her. The problem was that Shirley hated her grandmother. Or, rather, she hated the idea of living with her. Perhaps, it would be more correct to say that she hated the idea of no longer being able to live with the mother she so desperately loved. So she mostly ignored the old lady and kept to herself, hanging out in her room like a wraith—barely eating, hardly speaking and never smiling. The old lady had tried very hard to reach out to her granddaughter, and when Shirley was caught doing drugs in school, the grandmother had been horrified to be informed by the school counselor that the girl had made no attempt to even hide it. She sat in a very visible part of the school premises and used narcotics, apparently unconcerned that the authorities would catch her and report her.

When asked, Shirley had remained tight-lipped, until at long last she had admitted that she had *wanted* to be caught in the act. She had stolen money from her grandmother's cupboard, gone to her mother's old vendor and bought a stash, which she had saved up to use in school. When asked if Shirley used drugs at home, a weeping Rayhelle had assured them that she cleaned the girl's room herself most thoroughly every day, and had never come across any kind of drugs or narcotics till date.

'Well, that makes sense,' the counselor had replied thoughtfully.

'What does?' the old lady enquired.

'Shirley doesn't really want to do drugs for the sake of doing it, Mrs Carson. She only wanted to get caught doing it so that, by her logic, she will be put in prison and will be reunited with her mother, whom she misses.'

'But Shirley will not be sent to the prison where her mother has been imprisoned! She'll be sent to a place for minors—'

'Exactly!' the counselor had agreed. 'But she didn't realize that. She does now,' she had added hurriedly, when she saw the distress on the old lady's face.

All this had been shared with Sheela when she took up volunteering with the Girl Scouts of Central Maryland. Knowing Shirley's pain as she did, it was difficult for Sheela to stand by and watch the girl, who seemed so alone and morose while the others enjoyed themselves at Macy's. She walked up to stand beside her and said in her cheerful, kindly way, 'When I was a little girl, my grandmother always loved handkerchiefs. So, I would save up my pocket money and buy her some with her initials on it. Her name was Padmavathi, so I would get her hankies with the letter "P" embroidered onto them. They always made her so happy!'

Shirley didn't turn her head or acknowledge Sheela's words. But from a slight change in her body language, Sheela could tell that the young girl was listening. Sheela went on, 'When we swapped stories in school, I discovered that all my friends' grandmothers too loved hankies! I guess it's a grandmother thing. Wonder if we'll feel the same way once we grow older?'

Shirley slowly turned her head and looked at Sheela, her expression blank.

'What did your gran pack you for lunch today?' asked Sheela.

'Yogurt and ham sandwiches,' Shirley mumbled, looking away.

'Your favorite?'

Shirley nodded imperceptibly.

'Does she always make you lunch? Or do you carry lunch money?'

'She makes it.'

Sheela smiled. 'She must care about you a lot.'

Shirley frowned, as if this was a new thought to her. But Sheela was already moving towards the other girls, calling out to them saying, 'We have to get going, you guys. I still need to take you to the firm and show you around. Anybody who wants to get anything billed, this would be a good time to do so.'

The girls scurried around to finish any final purchases with the $50 gift cards that each of them had received that afternoon from Sheela. After that, the entire group trooped outside after Sheela. Sheela looked around to see that they were all there.

'Hey, where's Shirley?'

'She was billing something, Ms Murthy,' replied Judith.

'Oh, let's leave her,' said Makela, carelessly. 'She'll catch up!'

'Nothing doing,' said Sheela, turning to go back for Shirley, just as the girl came hurrying out of the store.

'Where were you?' asked Sheela in surprise, but Shirley didn't answer.

They crossed the street and made their way to the Murthy Law Firm building not far away. The girls stopped outside and stared up at the name on the top.

'This *your* office, Ms Murthy?' asked one of them in awe.

'Yes,' replied Sheela and led the way inside. When they walked into the lobby after her, the girls looked around, their jaws dropping open. They had never imagined this friendly, down-to-earth woman who volunteered to take them out and looked after them with such kindness, ran a place as grand and opulent as this! They looked at the logo of the firm on the wall with the head of Lady Liberty and streaks of red and blue behind it, and they whistled in appreciation!

'You're rich!' exclaimed one girl. 'Give me money!'

Sheela, who had been speaking with the security guard about the health of his child, spun around sharply at these words. 'No,' she said flatly. 'I got nothing for free, and you will get nothing for free from me. I worked fourteen, sometimes eighteen hours a day to get to where I am. And even after getting here, I still work long, long hours. My clients are people who are trying to come to America to get away from poverty, from political persecution, or sometimes for the chance to make a better life for themselves and their children. Whereas, you girls are *citizens* of America, just by virtue of the fact that you were born here. You have no idea how lucky you are! Now all you have to do is put in a bit of effort, and you'll have everything you ever dreamed of. I'll give you a job here if you want it and qualify. But I'll give you nothing for free.'

There was silence in the group. These girls who had always believed themselves to be unlucky were now, in effect, being told the exact opposite, and that too by someone they admired and respected. Suddenly, Sheela's stern face relaxed into a smile. 'Nobody gets a full cup. But what it really boils down to is this: How do *you* choose to see your cup? Half empty or half full? Your moms may not be able to be with you at the moment. But many of you have grandmothers who have taken on the role of caring for you, just so you will not have to go to foster homes. That sounds like a blessing to me!'

Many of the girls dropped their eyes when they heard this. So as not to make the lecture long or unpleasant, Sheela turned and moved towards the elevator. They continued on the tour of the firm, and Sheela introduced them to her team of lawyers over lunch. Their plates piled high with food, the Girl Scouts and the attorneys of MLF all sat around chatting.

'You'd better finish what's on your plate, you know?' said Anna teasingly to a girl called Brianna, who had taken an especially large helping. 'Sheela will get mad if you waste anything.' Brianna's eyes widened and she looked at Chloe in dismay. Khorzad had wandered up to join them.

'Really?' asked Brianna anxiously, glancing at him for confirmation.

'Yup. Oh, yes. She can get really mean,' replied Khorzad, suppressing a smile and nodding seriously.

'Is she a strict boss, then?' asked Chloe.

Both Anna and Khorzad, unable to pull it off any longer, started to laugh.

'Gosh, no, she's great! We were just kidding!' said Anna.

'Er … well not entirely about the food though,' added Khorzad. 'The thing is that Sheela is a foodie and she loves feeding people. But she also thinks that food should be respected and nobody should waste it. Tell them about your interview with MLF, Anna,' he urged.

'Oh that? Yeah,' said Anna, taking a bite of the taco and chewing on it before continuing. 'I joined the firm in 2007. Before they hired me, I had a phone interview, after which I was invited to visit the firm for an in-person meeting. I flew into Baltimore from Iowa, where I lived at the time, and stayed at a nearby hotel. The following morning, which was a Sunday, I came to the firm to meet with Sheela, Vasant and a few other attorneys. The meeting stretched on for a while, and then continued in a restaurant across the road where the entire group was treated to lunch. As we were entering the place, Vasant turned to me and said in an undertone, "Sheela likes it when people eat. Make sure you finish your meal." I did not have much of an appetite thanks to all the excitement and adrenaline rushing through my blood, given that I was being interviewed. But I tried to keep the food going in, and to respond to questions at the same time with as much grace as I could muster. On the way out, I turned to Vasant and asked, "How did I do with the food?" When he gave me a thumbs up, I knew I did fine! The food continues to be an important part of the culture of our firm, as you can see.' Anna nodded towards the well-stocked table nearby. 'Sheela loves taking care of us and making sure everyone is well-fed.'

'Well-stuffed, you mean!' corrected Khorzad. And as if on cue, Sheela wandered up to the girls innocently and asked, 'Is everybody eating well? Chloe, can I get you anything? Come on, have another burrito.' The second the words were out of her mouth, the four of them were rolling with laughter! Sheela watched them, bemused, for a whole minute. When the mirth showed no signs of abating, she shrugged resignedly and wandered away to check on the next group.

'She's really very nice, isn't she?' asked Brianna.

'She's the best!' replied Khorzad. 'You'd never know that she was that brilliant and that successful because she has no airs about her. One time she invited a group for dinner to her place, and the food was outstanding! The daal, the vegetables, the side snacks, they were absolutely delicious. The flavors literally exploded in your mouth! Rushna, my wife, and I had been planning to have a little get-together for our friends to celebrate our daughter, Meher, turning one. That night, at Sheela's place, we decided that we definitely wanted to go with the same people who had catered for this party. After dinner, Rushna asked Sheela which restaurant she had ordered the food from. Sheela looked surprised and said she had cooked everything herself.'

The girls looked impressed, and Anna, who was familiar with their backgrounds, also knew that this was a good opportunity to impress upon them a lesson in goodness and decency—just something for them to turn over in their minds on days when the going got rough. So, she narrated another anecdote.

'Sheela is down to earth. When I first joined the firm, on my very first day at work, I was getting familiar with various programs on my computer, which included an internal instant messenger. The version of the program the firm was using at the time was equipped with pre-written messages, such as "On my way" and "I will get back to you soon." While trying to learn the program, I unintentionally sent Sheela a pre-written instant message, which said, "Come to my office." Once I realized my mistake, I was horrified and did not know how to fix it. Almost immediately, she arrived in my office and asked if there was anything she could do to help. I apologized and explained my mistake. She just laughed it off and said it was no big deal!'

'I'd like to work for her someday,' said Brianna.

'Me too!' agreed Chloe.

'Then maybe you will,' said Khorzad, kindly. 'We'd be happy to have you here. But you girls will have to work very hard because Sheela will never give the job to someone who is careless or takes short cuts. Her clients mean more to her than anything in the world, and this firm is her baby!'

At the next table, Shirley and three other girl scouts were eating lunch with attorneys Pamela Genise, Alissa Klein and Adam Rosen. As soon as they had finished and put away their plates, they took out their shopping and showed them to the women, who examined the little knick-knacks with interest. Sheela who was watching discreetly from across the room saw Shirley hesitate until everyone else was done. Then, slowly, she removed a small package from inside her old rucksack and showed it to Pamela. Pamela unwrapped the parcel, handling it like it was an important thing. She withdrew the contents. There were three handkerchiefs with the initials 'R' embroidered on them. Rayhella! Instinctively Shirley looked across the room to where Sheela was standing and watching her. The fourteen-year-old gave Sheela a small, tentative smile. Sheela smiled back with her heart in her eyes.

37

Kate Jentz of Carmel, Indiana, had first read out her poem at the naturalization ceremony, sponsored by the MurthyNAYAK Foundation, in Indianapolis. Kate's grandmother had fled war-torn Spain in her youth, and arrived in the United States as a refugee. Several decades later, Kate had been born in America. After that first reading of her poem, Kate read it a second time, one warm June day of 2019, at the Foundation's American Immigration Council's annual gala. The gala was held that year at the Convention Center in Orlando, Florida. Kate's had been the winning poem. When she reached the end of her reading, the applause was thunderous! Her old grandmother, Kate's *abuela*, sat there in the audience, beaming with a silent sense of pride in her beloved grandchild and her marvelous pen!

Each year, since 1997, the American Immigration Council (AIC or the Council) organized the Celebrate America Creative Writing Contest held at the same location where AILA held its annual conference. The event had been an initiative of the MurthyNAYAK Foundation. Children from across the country were invited to write a poem on the theme, *Why I Am Grateful America is a Nation of Immigrants*. Thousands of children, many among them immigrants or second-generation immigrants, participated with real gusto. That year, in 2019, Kate had won the big prize. The prior year, in 2018, the winner had been Imyra Guerrero of Roslindale, Massachusetts, whose father had migrated to the United States from Honduras. And before that, a young resident of California, an immigrant from the Middle East, had taken home the prize.

The Council, of which Sheela was a trustee, worked hard to get more and more middle school children to participate. This was one of their tools to empower and educate Americans to explore their own past, and embrace the fact that their country's true identity is in its humble beginnings, as a nation of immigrants. The Council hoped that through efforts like this, America would remember and celebrate its immigrant roots. It would remember to be proud to embrace its immigrant past instead of feeling ashamed about it.

When, in 2014, Sheela Murthy made her $1 million multi-year pledge to the AIC, she became its single largest donor. She was accorded the honor of announcing the winners of the essay contest each year at the annual gala. Back in June 2017, Sheela had announced the name of the winner and invited her to read her poem. The girl had come up on stage and said, with a bright smile, 'I am glad that the US is a nation of immigrants because it brings culture, experiences and foods to our lives. Oh, and also because, without immigration, a lot of us would not be here!' The audience had gone into splits at this candid summation of the entire night's event! When the laughter subsided, the young poet had proceeded to read her entry in a sing-song voice, drawing enthusiastic applause and a standing ovation.

The following year, in June 2018, Imyra had been invited to read out her poem. Imyra had slowly risen to her feet and made her way up to the stage.

'My poem was inspired by my father's story,' she had begun. 'Things were terrible for his family in Honduras because they lost everything. But my papa did not give up.' Her eyes strayed to her father, and he looked down because there were too many things in his heart at that moment and he was afraid they would spill into his eyes for everyone to see. 'He came to America and began a new life for us,' Imyra had continued, 'and that is why now I'm American. America is my country and I'm happy to live here in a nice house among kind people who will not try to kill us and destroy our home like they did in Honduras.'

She had spoken simply. The audience waited in silence, digesting the words of the ten-year-old, and the matter-of-fact way in which she had spoken of death, the gratitude with which she had described life. Into the silence she had read her poem titled, 'The Blessing of Immigration'. Her voice had been quiet and measured, unexpected for one so young. When she reached the end of it, she raised her eyes and looked around the room shyly. There had been a smattering of applause. But mostly, people had sat silently, moved by the words that still lingered in the air. A few people had cried a little, people had forgotten to clap or cheer. And so, Imyra had given a little bow and left the stage, clutching the paper to her heart as she went.

The poems of the three winners had captured the essence of what it was like for individuals and families who had left their homeland and come to the United States. Some had left by choice, others out of necessity. Then there were those who had been driven away. But these children, who wrote with such clarity, had been touched by a past that had failed to embitter. These were the ones—whether their poems won or did not—who looked through eyes uncolored by prejudice and only saw a future that was filled with hope and new possibilities. 'This is life. This is what it means to live,' thought Sheela, sitting among the audience. And once again, she knew herself to be lucky and blessed to be a woman of color, an immigrant, one who had left her family, home and her country out of her own free will, to study, find work, success and friendships that fulfilled, without dimming the beauty of all she had left behind. Some of those things that people had believed to be her liabilities, she had taken and turned into her greatest assets and strengths. For this, Sheela was grateful.

38

On 7 May 2019, Murthy Law Firm completed twenty-five years of its existence. Vasant and Sheela held a grand celebration in a hotel ballroom in Towson, not far from the firm in Owings Mills. To this event, they invited all the attorneys and the staff of MLF with their families, as well as some dear friends of Sheela and Vasant. The guest list was numbered at a hundred. The celebration was grand, not because it was opulent, but because people attended with real pride and joy at the firm having reached such a milestone.

'There are only two ways to leave Murthy Law Firm!' joked Sheela in her speech that evening, 'You retire, or you die!' Everyone grinned, Khorzad in particular, who had taken a hiatus from MLF to explore other opportunities before he missed 'home' so badly that he returned to the firm a few years later.

'I am able to celebrate this milestone because of all of you,' went on Sheela. 'When I first started Murthy Law Firm, I was lonely. I worked. I slogged from sun up to well past sundown because I was terrified that I would slip up somewhere, fail to cover some aspect of a case and end up letting my clients down. But then, one by one you guys came on board. Now, I've forgotten what it is like to be lonely or frightened. I know you guys are with me, and that you have my back, so how can anything go wrong? It's a team effort to help our clients—from answering the phone and prepping documents to implementing legal strategy. Everything, every single thing that each one of you does here is important for the success of this firm. Before you guys first joined MLF, I always told you at your interviews that I don't care how much you know until I know how much you care. But very quickly I saw how deeply all of you cared. What you've handled at the firm are not cases. They haven't been just work to you. They have been labors of love, and that has been evident in everything you've done, and in the fact that today we can count ourselves among the finest immigration law firms in the world. Your presence gives me something to thank god for every day, and I—'

Here, Sheela broke down, overwhelmed, and Vasant held her as he blinked back his own tears. The others crowded around them, holding on to each other without words. For there was very little of the feeling in the room, at that moment, that could possibly be expressed in words. Sometimes the moment just speaks for itself.

* * *

That night, after they returned home from the celebration, tired but happy, Vasant went to bed early. But Sheela sat up reading for a while. Immigration was her life. It was the thing, next to Vasant, that she loved best in the world. Inside the book she was reading was a piece of paper tucked away. This was something she had asked little Imyra for in June 2018 at the Council's gala; the young girl had diligently copied it out for her and tucked the folded piece of paper into her hand at the end of the evening, before they had parted ways. Sheela had wanted it as a keepsake, in memory of the motherless child who had captured her heart by her simple, unadulterated perspective of an immigrant's experience of America.

She often took out that piece of paper, written over with Imyra's poem, and read it to herself. Tonight, by the soft glow of her bedside lamp, Sheela read it again.

THE BLESSING OF IMMIGRATION

It's Gone
Everything
Gone
My home
My mom
My family
My childhood
Thinking
No me gusta!
But there's nothing I can do
I didn't want this to happen
But it did
I could not change anything
If I had one wish
I would stay

Left
I left everything
My mom

My friends
My home
Todas

My New Home
America
Boston
English
I was so confused
Overwhelmed
"What do I do now?"
Adiós Honduras

Adiós
I said *Adiós*
But I want to say it again
So,
Adiós, mamá,
Adiós, amigos,
Adiós, mi vida

Fit In
I didn't know what they were saying
Mi papá told me that we were in Boston
That they spoke English
I went to school
People didn't say "*Hola.*"
Instead they said "Hi."
But I didn't

English

"How do I speak it?"
¿Cómo se dice?
"*Yo no sé*," *Papá* says,
"We will learn soon."
I didn't fit in

Maple Street

I saw this girl,
She taught me.
She taught me how to speak English!
Estaba tan feliz

Nikki

Is from Boston
She's different
Smart
Sassy
Funny
Mi amiga, mi hermana

My New Family

Friends
Family all happy
Because of my new *amiga*,

Imyra

I will never forget
The best day of my life,

Moving to America
I didn't know it yet,
But soon I did

Now
Ahora, este país es mi casa,
I live here,
I have family and friends here,
America!

How could a child who had lost her mother, her home, her world
so suddenly, be so full of hope? Was it a quality of childhood? Or
perhaps of humanity in general—the irrepressible, unconquerable
human spirit that rises and rises again in the face of pain, hardship and
apparent defeat? Sheela knew herself to be part of this struggle—the
struggle for justice, equality and for the inclusion of all humankind,
regardless of gender, color or creed. Sheela had her firm. She had her
team to fight by her side. She looked at Vasant sleeping beside her,
watched the steady rise and fall of his chest, and a sense of well-being
filled her soul. She had this man, this loyal friend and companion,
beside her now, and he would be there in the morning when she
woke up. She folded the piece of paper and carefully slipped it into
her book, turned off the light and settled down to sleep.

Acknowledgements

I would like to thank my aunt, Mrs Sheila Rao, for the lessons she has taught me in grace, stability and dignity, by being all of those things herself. At every step of the book's journey, her inputs and advice have been invaluable.

My gratitude to Vasant and Sheela for entrusting to me the writing of this book that has been their long-cherished dream. Sheela cheerfully shared her stories over countless cups of green tea, delicious food and delightful digressions in conversation (when two Librans get together, it is unreasonable to expect brevity!), making work seem like play. Her patient and meticulous explanation of the workings of US immigration law is much appreciated.

Prema Govindan, with characteristic insight, wit and sagacity, turned this venture into something far beyond what any of us had envisioned! Working with her is always a joy because, aside of being my editor, she is a dear friend.

Last and definitely not least, many thanks to Rakesh Chander and Latha Nair for steering this ship safely to the harbor.

About the Author

After a degree in theater from Smith College, Massachusetts, Adithi Rao worked as an assistant director on the award-winning Hindi film *Satya*, and then as writer/editor on the travel channel, Indya.com.

Adithi published her debut novel, *Left from the Nameless Shop*, with HarperCollins India. She has written books for children too: *Candid Tales: India on a Motorcycle*, *Growing up in Pandupur*, *Chuchu Manthu's Jar of Toffees* and *Shakuntala and other Timeless Tales of Ancient India*. Her short stories and non-fiction work have appeared in anthologies across leading publishing houses and several American literary journals.

The rights to her film scripts have been bought by Aamir Khan Productions Ltd and Excel Entertainment.

Adithi is currently scripting a play for Katkatha Puppet Arts Trust, and conducts writing workshops for children and adults.

You can find her on adithirao.com.